Powerlifting

Mastering the Skills for an Empowered Body and Life

(A Two-a-day Long Cycle & Powerlifting Training Program for Intermediate Lifters)

Louis Davis

Published By **Tyson Maxwell**

Louis Davis

Powerlifting: Mastering the Skills for an Empowered Body and Life (A Two-a-day Long Cycle & Powerlifting Training Program for Intermediate Lifters)

ISBN   978-1-7753142-8-8

Legal & Disclaimer

The information contained in this book is not designed to replace or take the place of any form of medicine or professional medical advice. The information in this book has been provided for educational & entertainment purposes only.

The information contained in this book has been compiled from sources deemed reliable, and it is accurate to the best of the Author's knowledge; however, the Author cannot guarantee its accuracy and validity and cannot be held liable for any errors or omissions. Changes are periodically made to this book. You must consult your doctor or get professional medical advice before using any of the suggested remedies, techniques, or information in this book.

Table Of Contents

Chapter 1: The Four Phases For Building Maximum Strength

Four Components of the Training System

If your intention is to benefit strength, it typically takes more than one form of education to build the numerous physical traits that make a contribution to maximum electricity profits. The 4 segment exercising offers an answer that will help you gain this. Each workout addresses the electricity improving features inclusive of: rapid strain manufacturing, strength, muscular increase, and workload ability. When the ones attributes are professional efficaciously, they work together to help you gather strength on a consistent foundation. The 4 degrees that help you accomplish this are indexed under.

1. The Power Warm up

For growing: Speed, speedy pressure production, and explosive power

2. Ascending Single Reps

For developing: Strength

3. Mini Sets or Half Sets

For developing: Strength, power, and muscle length

four. Full Sets

For developing: Muscle length, capillary improvement, and electricity

The Most Powerful Strength Building Exercises

What are the basics of a famous 4 segment workout? First, it's far designed to be easy in terms of exercise preference. The physical video games need to include essential compound sporting activities that artwork the three most effective muscle organizations which have the nice capability for gaining energy. These 3 muscle companies are indexed inside the chart under on the side of the sporting sports that artwork them:

Three Strongest Muscle Groups

1. Leg/Glute Muscles	2. Back Muscles	3. Chest (pec) Muscles
Exercises for Legs and glutes	Exercises for Back Muscles	Exercises for Chest Muscles
1. Squats	1. Seated Pulley Rows	1. Bench Press
2. Front Squats	2. Bent over Barbell Rows	2. Incline Press
3. Deadlifts	3. Lat Pull downs	3. Dips (medium to wide grip)
4. Leg Press	4. Pull ups	4. Upright Shoulder Press
When doing the exercises listed above, the following smaller muscle groups (listed below) assist the bigger muscle groups with the lifting action		
1. Core Stability Muscles Abdominals Oblique Muscles Lower Back	1. Bicep muscles of the arms 2. Rear deltoid muscles of the shoulders	1. Triceps muscles of the arms 2. Front and side deltoid muscles of the shoulders

Secondary Muscle Groups

Notice that whilst you do number one compound physical video games for the three biggest muscle corporations, you may moreover be workout severa smaller muscle agencies that assist the bigger muscle organizations. For example, while doing urgent sporting activities for the chest (or pectoral) muscle tissues, you could moreover be running the triceps muscular tissues of the decrease lower back of the fingers, and the deltoid muscular tissues of the shoulders. When doing pulling bodily video video games for the another time muscular tissues, you may moreover be running the bicep muscle groups of the palms, further to the rear deltoid muscle businesses of the shoulders. When doing squatting and deadlift physical sports for the leg/glute muscle corporations, you could also be going for walks the middle balance muscle companies of the front abs, factor obliques, and decrease decrease again.

Three Main Exercises consistent with Workout

You don't need to do thousands of various sporting occasions to gain power. When you choose your bodily sports activities effectively, it only takes 3 essential physical sports to cowl the three maximum effective muscle companies, and severa other muscle agencies can be worked inside the approach. Each exercising have to encompass a leg/glute exercise, a lower once more exercise, and a chest (pectoral) exercising

Easy Recovery Enables High Frequency Training

One of the motives for focusing on just 3 sports activities consistent with workout is that the 4 section training device is designed to be a high frequency training application that may be completed three or greater times in line with week. In order to training

4

consultation three to 6 days consistent with week, the workout workouts must be smooth to get over. Doing too many wearing sports makes it hard to get over exercise workouts. Doing some clean sports activities activities in combination with the right quantity of units, and the right quantity of strive, will make it easy in order to recover from your sporting activities.

Alternative Exercises

The essential bodily games that you can see at the following couple of pages have established to be effective for multitudes of people from every the past and present. It is pretty viable that you have get right of entry to to weight schooling machines which you choose to use instead of the free weight physical activities which can be verified within the subsequent segment. It is perfectly great to alternative sporting sports you opt for for the physical games in this e-book. However, even if you pick out out to use weight education machines, I strongly suggest that you attention on pressing and pulling wearing activities with machines, in choice to isolation physical video video games that art work sincerely one muscle organization at a time.

Isolation Exercises

Examples of isolation physical video games are dumbbell flies, cable flies, percent deck flies, dumbbell will growth to the the the the front, once more, or factor, system lateral will increase, bicep curls, triceps extensions, hyperextensions, dumbbell pullovers, system pullovers, shrugs, curl ups, calf raises, leg curls, and leg extension. As you could see, there are multitudes of isolation physical sports activities that might add as a lot as massive exercise workout routines if you try and do all of them. Isolation bodily games are not wrong or awful, however they aren't as effective for building not unusual strength.

Choosing Exercises

If you want to exercising consultation, you may probable enjoy compelled to do greater than three fundamental bodily sports activities. If that is the case, you may gain from along with some isolation sporting sports which might be each completed for one set of 8 to 12 repetitions. However, I strongly suggest that you preserve your exercise exercises quick and smooth. If your primary focus is to assemble electricity, talk to the number one sports activities which are established within the subsequent segment through choosing one squatting/deadlift exercising, one urgent exercise for the chest, and one pulling workout for the back.

Chapter 2: The Four Phase Workout

The mystery to meaking number one sports activities artwork is to layout a ordinary so as to utilize them inside the maximum efficient manner feasible. The 4 phase exercise is the solution for this and a pattern of three first rate exercise workout routines is supplied on the following 3 pages. Each workout includes four tiers, however they range in period consistent with your non-public workload functionality. The eight Set Workout is indexed first because it gives a starting point to assess your workload capability. If it isn't sufficient paintings, you could regulate as a great deal as the ten Set Workout, and if it is an excessive amount of art work, you may reduce down on the workload thru doing the 7 Set Workout. More may be discussed in regard to adjustments to exercising exercises in the direction of the stop of the e-book.

eight Sets in step with Exercise Workout: 30 to 40 Minutes

Instructions: Do 3 number one compound carrying sports collectively with:

1. A squat or deadlift exercising for leg/glute muscle mass

2. A pressing workout for chest, triceps, and deltoid muscle mass

3. A pulling workout for lower back, biceps and rear deltoid muscle groups

Use the following gadgets, reps, and weight for each exercising:

Phase 1: Power Warm up Sets

Set #1: 10 reps: Use a weight that allows 30 robust reps, however splendid do 10 reps

Set #2: 6 reps: Use a weight that permits 18 strong reps, however handiest do 6 reps

Phase 2: Ascending Single Reps

Set #3: 1 rep: Use a weight that allows eight sturdy reps, however best do 1 rep

Set #four: 1 rep: Use a weight that permits four sturdy reps, however handiest do 1 rep

Set #5: 1 rep: Use your single rep education max weight

Phase 3: Half Sets or Mini Sets

Set #6: five reps: Use a weight that permits eight to ten sturdy reps, however first-rate do five reps.

Set #7: five reps: Use a weight that permits eight to ten robust reps, however tremendous do 5 reps.

Phase four: Full Sets

Set #8: 12-15 reps: Use weight that lets in a sturdy rep max of 12 to 15 reps.

Training Frequency and rest among Sets

-Do the eight set exercising three to 6 instances consistent with week

-Rest 30 to 45 seconds amongst gadgets 1-4

-Rest 90 seconds earlier than doing set 5, 6, and seven

-Rest 2 to three minutes in advance than doing set 8

Please Note: The term robust reps and strong rep max are described in chapter 7, and the time period single rep education max is defined in bankruptcy 8.

Click proper right right here for a printable pdf version of the eight set exercise

10 Sets consistent with Exercise Workout: 36 to 45 Minutes

Instructions: Do 3 essential compound sporting activities which includes:

1. A squat or deadlift exercising for leg/glute muscle organizations

2. A urgent exercise for chest, triceps, and deltoid muscle businesses

3. A pulling exercise for again, biceps and rear deltoid muscle corporations

Use the subsequent units, reps, and weight for each exercise:

Phase 1: Power Warm up Sets

Set #1: 10 reps: Use a weight that permits 30 robust reps, however incredible do 10 reps

Set # 2: 8 reps: Use a weight that lets in 24 strong reps, but best do eight reps.

Set #3: 6 reps: Use a weight that allows 18 robust reps, however simplest do 6 reps

Phase 2: Ascending Single Reps

Set #4: 1 rep: Use a weight that allows 12 strong reps, however simplest do 1 rep

Set #5: 1 rep: Use a weight that lets in eight strong reps, but super do 1 rep

Set #6: 1 rep: Use a weight that permits 4 strong reps, but nice do 1 rep

Set #7: 1 rep: Use your single rep schooling max weight

Phase three: Half Sets or Mini Sets

Set #eight: 5 reps: Use a weight that lets in eight to ten robust reps, however best do 5 reps.

Set #nine: 5 reps: Use a weight that lets in 8 to ten strong reps, but only do 5 reps.

Phase 4: Full Sets

Set #10: 12-15 reps: Use weight that allows a sturdy rep max of 12 to fifteen reps.

Training Frequency and relaxation among Sets

-Do the ten set exercise 3 to six instances in line with week

-Rest 30 to forty five seconds amongst sets 1-6

-Rest ninety seconds in advance than doing set 7, 8, and 9

-Rest 2 to a few minutes before doing set 10

Please Note: The term strong reps and strong rep max are described in bankruptcy 7, and the term unmarried rep schooling max is described in monetary destroy 8.

Click right proper right here for a printable pdf model of the ten Set workout

7 Sets in line with Exercise Workout: 25 to 35 Minutes

Instructions: Do 3 easy compound bodily activities along aspect:

1. A squat or deadlift workout for leg/glute muscle tissue

2. A urgent workout for chest, triceps, and deltoid muscle groups

3. A pulling exercising for returned, biceps and rear deltoid muscle tissues

Use the following devices, reps, and weight for every exercise:

Phase 1: Power Warm up Sets

Set #1: 10 reps: Use a weight that lets in 30 strong reps, but best do 10 reps

Set #2: 6 reps: Use a weight that lets in 18 sturdy reps, however only do 6 reps

Phase 2: Ascending Single Reps

Set #3: 1 rep: Use a weight that lets in 12 robust reps, but best do 1 rep

Set #four: 1 rep: Use a weight that allows eight robust reps, however only do 1 rep

Set #five: 1 rep: Use a weight that allows 4 robust reps, but handiest do 1 rep

Phase three: Half Sets or Mini Sets

Set #6: five reps: Use a weight that permits 8 to ten robust reps, but simplest do 5 reps.

Phase 4: Full Sets

Set #7: 12-15 reps: Use weight that permits a robust rep max of 12 to fifteen reps.

Training Frequency and relaxation among Sets

-Do the 7 set exercising 3 to six instances in step with week

-Rest 30 to 45 seconds among devices 1-5

-Rest 90 seconds before doing gadgets 6

-Rest 2 to 3 minutes in advance than doing set 7

Please Note: The term sturdy reps and sturdy rep max are defined in bankruptcy 7, and the time period unmarried rep education max is defined in bankruptcy 8.

Click right here for a printable pdf model of the 7 set exercise

Chapter 3: Things That Make Your Workouts Work

Flexible Use of Training Phases

The fundamental exercise can without issues be modified to address your desires and training capability. You can add or subtract gadgets from the primary exercise in keeping with your workload capability, and you could delete tiers and encompass degrees consistent with your dreams.

Fast Paced Workouts

As you can see, the workout routines encompass doing a large quantity of units without very a bargain relaxation amongst gadgets at some point of stages one and . This is because of the truth the sets in tiers one and aren't taxing (besides for your single rep training max), and don't require the want for lots of relaxation so that it will get higher. You will honestly keep away from the fine and snug up approach in case you rest too prolonged among the exceptional and relaxed up devices as it will purpose you to cool off. The workout slows down whilst you reach levels 3 and four because the units turn out to be more hard.

There is a advocated time frame indexed above every exercising that offers you an concept of the manner lengthy a exercise should take. The time body gives you the selection for using a quicker exercising pace, or a slower workout pace. Do your awesome no longer to head over the time range indexed for every exercising, and in case you want some cardiovascular experience the exercising routines, shoot for the faster time.

While it doesn't harm to push your self to finish each workout at a fairly short pace, don't push to the point in that you are truely out of breath for the entire exercise. You received't be capable of increase as heavy while you are constantly out of breath. It is important to learn how to push difficult enough, but no longer too difficult.

Work out Just Enough however Not Too Much

The vital concept in the again of the four section carrying occasions is to educate simply sufficient, but no extra than vital to stimulate a fantastic schooling impact. The exercising in all fairness focused on using the ATP creatine phosphate strength device, it truly is the power machine for your muscle companies this is used for energy, velocity, electricity, and speedy stress production. This technique that the majority of the weight schooling is completed in brief bursts, the use of quick reps, and quick sets. Training on this manner prevents the buildup fatigue, that could intervene with power development.

Work out Often: Three to Six Time consistent with Week

When you restriction your training to only some carrying sports, and your gadgets are hard sufficient but not too hard, it makes recuperation amongst workout workouts smooth. When recovery is easy, you can teach regularly with out overtraining. Instead of doing workout routines which might be prolonged and difficult, you do physical video games which can be brief and tough enough, however now not too difficult. This lets in you to educate your entire frame (or each muscle group) three to 6 times consistent with week, in order to preserve your stage of herbal anabolic hormones accelerated on a constant foundation to sell strength earnings.

The 4 phase exercise gadget is primarily based completely mostly on education at a fairly cushty stage of hassle on a common foundation, as opposed to to do severe bodily activities lots a good deal less frequently. Severe exercise physical activities generally purpose an excessive amount of fatigue and result in the overuse of the lactate electricity device on the way to compromise energy earnings. The purpose for preserving off excessive sports isn't to break out difficult schooling, but to growth the effectiveness of long term schooling consequences.

Forceful Lifting

An important element to all 4 degrees is the idea of utilising most stress into each rep. While it's miles real that doing the right quantity of devices and reps is crucial, if that's all you cognizance on, then you may pass over one of the most critical factors of education, that is strain production on each rep. If you don't exercise maximum pressure, you may't expect maximum nerve firing, maximum muscle fiber recruitment, or most results.

Lift Faster First, Then upload Weight

The machine for progressing and enhancing may be very essential. While many power education techniques in fashionable interest on including weight or reps which will beautify, the number one reputation for development even as using the four section exercise device is to first enhance your capability to raise a given weight faster and much less complex.

Follow Your Body's Goal for Getting Strong

Follow the Primary Goal of Your Body

The important cause your body desires to advantage electricity is in reality to gain its purpose of making it lots much less difficult that allows you to carry a given weight. A thoughts-set which uses strategies which is probably based totally totally on finding tactics to teach more hard and extra difficult on the way to maintain gaining power is honestly contrary to what your body is making an attempt to perform on the same time as it gains power. The constant try to make workout workouts extra hard defeats the entire reason of why your frame wants to get stronger. Since your frame income strength that will help you raise the weights much less complex, deliver it a enough time period to carry out this aim with the aid of way of permitting the equal weights to grow to be a good deal less tough to raise as you advantage power.

Eventually you may upload weight to your physical video games. Adding weight will growth the issue of the exercise, but if you normally allow the load you're the use of turn out to be a lot less hard first, then an increase in weight want to revel in no more tough than the final time you delivered weight. For instance, in case you are growing from a hundred thirty five pounds to a hundred and forty pounds, then one hundred forty kilos need to sense no more hard to reinforce than whilst you first extended from a hundred thirty pounds to 130 5 kilos.

Clarification of Easier

When I take a look at with permitting a weight to end up simpler to reinforce, I need to clarify that you'll be the use of some of weights and reps for one in each of a kind devices for the duration of a exercise, however that identical type of weights and reps want for use from one exercising to the following until the weights being used for every set turns into less complicated. We will imagine for a 2d that your exercise encompass plenty of weights that consist of 75 pounds, ninety 5 kilos, a hundred twenty 5 kilos, a hundred fifty kilos, 100 75 kilos, 205 kilos, 225 kilos, one hundred 75 kilos, and 100 45 kilos for an exercising. Each amount of weight indexed will be assigned some of reps which you are to perform. These equal weights and reps want to be continuously used from one exercising to the subsequent till each exercising poundage may be lifted faster and simpler before adding extra weight.

Many human beings recollect that you must continuously alternate the quantity of weight and reps from one exercise to the subsequent, or your bodily activities may be useless. This is real in case you habitually train too tough, but, while the use of the 4 phase training system, you may no longer be education too hard, and will learn how to educate at a particular degree of attempt. One of the number one strategies to recognise whether or not or now not you are training too difficult or not is to apprehend the difference amongst robust education and inclined training. This might be mentioned inside the next section.

Exceedingly Important: Train Strong to Get Strong

A crucial strength education idea this is of high-quality importance is which you need to train sturdy to get strong. Knowing how hard to educate is based mostly on staying inside the limitations of robust training, and heading off vulnerable training. Reps can be strong or susceptible, gadgets may be sturdy or susceptible, and your lifting motion for heavy unmarried reps may be sturdy or susceptible. You can differentiate between sturdy education and prone training whilst you recognize schooling thresholds.

Key Concept: Base your schooling spherical pushing to threshold capacities with out exceeding those capacities

An pretty large, particularly essential problem that is included into the 4 segment schooling sports is the concept of thresholds (that is vital). Thresholds are primarily based mostly on your non-public power precise capacities. When you educate with precision via pushing right as much as the training thresholds, you can project the numerous strength unique capacities to increase.

Chapter 4: Strong Reps Vs. Weak Reps

One of the important thing thoughts that is used in the Four Phase Training device is the idea of robust reps. A sturdy rep can handiest be done at the same time as a lifter possesses enough strength to perform forceful reps the usage of a everyday even tempo from one rep to the following at some stage in a set. A susceptible rep happens on the identical time as sufficient fatigue is gift to prevent a lifter from being able to carry forcefully, and they're capable of now not keep a steady even tempo from one rep to the subsequent inside the route of a tough and speedy. This manner that lifting pressure starts to lower and the rep pace from one rep to the following starts offevolved to slow down subsequently of a tough and rapid. Strong reps are the focus of the four section schooling device, and prone reps are usually avoided.

Key Concept: The robust rep max is the right detail wherein you ought to prevent at the same time as doing a full set

The Strong Rep Max

Strong reps are as a foundation for figuring out in which to save you for the duration of a entire set. The last robust rep that you may perform with a given weight identifies the restriction of your capacity for sturdy reps during a hard and rapid. The maximum quantity of sturdy reps you could do interior a hard and rapid is referred to as your strong rep max. To be smooth, if you could do ten robust reps earlier than your rep tempo starts offevolved to sluggish down, then your robust rep max is ten reps for the quantity of weight you are the usage of for that exercise. When identifying your robust rep max, it's far vital which you make a deliberate try to perform your reps the use of a ordinary even tempo from one rep to the following. When acting a whole set, save you on the very last rep wherein you can hold a constant even rep pace. This especially applies to segment 4 even as doing the ultimate set for an workout.

Pushing a hard and fast beyond your sturdy rep max will start to emphasize staying electricity that is derived from the lactate power tool. Overemphasizing the lactate machine can also additionally help you to decorate your capacity to do extra prone reps on the cease of a tough and speedy with out enhancing your capacity to do greater strong reps at the start of the set. This will high-quality can help you teach longer without assisting you to make bigger stronger.

How to Lift Strong With Heavy Weights

A Strong Lifting Motion vs. A Weak Lifting Motion

We have already noted sturdy reps and inclined reps, and this could furthermore observe to heavy unmarried reps. A heavy unmarried rep can be lifted with a strong lifting movement, but if the load is simply too heavy, it will in all likelihood be lifted with a inclined lifting movement. A weight that is heavy enough to purpose a susceptible lifting movement is the form of rep which can have a terrible impact on strength profits when it is finished on a high frequency foundation.

The All-Out Single Rep Max

An all-out unmarried rep max is an instance of a weight this is too heavy to be used for schooling on a excessive frequency foundation. An all-out max is the most weight that could probably be lifted for a single rep. It is normally observed by means of a inclined lifting motion that still may be referred to as a grinder rep.

Grinder Reps: Avoid Them

A grinder rep is a rep that slows down or has points of pausing or hesitation at some diploma in the lifting movement. The lifter can't preserve a easy even lifting movement for the duration of the rep, and is pressured to strain or slowly grind out the rep in order to finish the decorate. This is what is supposed with the beneficial aid of a inclined lifting movement. When doing a heavy unmarried rep, a vulnerable lifting motion is a trademark that the weight is clearly too heavy for optimum power schooling.

Key Concept: The Single rep education max allows you pick out out the heaviest weight to educate with for strength profits.

The Single Rep Training Max

The most weight that need to be used for heavy unmarried reps is called a single rep education max (or in reality a training max). A education max is genuinely the heaviest single rep that may be done with a robust lifting movement. A robust lifting motion includes a clean, nonstop lifting movement without a breakdown in lifting shape. You should no longer want to psych your self up for this, nor need to there be any grinding, stalling, or slowing down in a few unspecified time in the destiny for the duration of the lifting movement, or the training max has been passed. Any time weight is added to a schooling max, you want to even though be capable of use a strong lifting motion with real shape. If a sturdy lifting motion can't be completed whilst weight is introduced, you need to pass once more to the previous weight you have been the use of and attention on gaining power through enhancing your functionality to elevate your cutting-edge training max faster and simpler. Once this has been performed to a sufficient degree, you ought on the way to upload weight at the same time as keeping a sturdy lifting movement.

Strong Sets Build Strong Muscles

Strong Sets and Weak Sets

Just as there are robust reps and prone reps, there are also sturdy gadgets and willing sets. Strong gadgets are clearly devices which may be completed at the same time as you are at complete electricity. Weak devices are units which is probably finished while you aren't at complete energy. I advise education to the limit of your capability of robust devices with out exceeding this capability via doing vulnerable gadgets. Train at complete energy the usage of robust gadgets to bring together robust muscle mass.

Key Concept: Your capability for strong devices determines how many units you need to do for a muscle institution.

Being at full power is based totally mostly on understanding in which your strong rep max takes place at the same time as you are warmed up with none fatigue to compromise your power. Once you understand your sturdy rep max at the equal time as the usage of a given weight for an workout, you have were given a gauge for knowing whether or not or not you are at full energy any time you operate that equal weight and workout. An example will assist to make clear this.

Let us recall that you are fully warmed up, but have now not superior any fatigue to compromise your strength; in specific terms, you are at entire energy. You load the bar to 225 pounds and do a set of squats to discover your sturdy rep max, which ultimately finally ends up being twelve reps. This can now be used as a gauge for expertise whether or no longer or no longer or now not you're at entire energy any time you're the usage of 225 kilos within the squat. If you fall brief of twelve robust reps with 225 kilos in the squat, you are not at complete electricity.

Your Last Set is a Gauge for Determining in case you are at Full Strength

When the usage of the four segment education gadget, your final set for an exercise or muscle group serves as a gauge for understanding whether or not or no longer you are but at whole energy. In the exercises indexed on the begin of the ebook, your remaining set for a muscle organisation will both be your 8th, 10th, or 7th set, relying on which exercise you use.

We will agree with which you are doing the eight set workout, and also you apprehend that your strong rep max with 225 kilos within the squat is twelve reps. If you can perform twelve sturdy reps with 225 kilos in your very last set, you recognize you have got been at entire power for the complete exercise, which incorporates the remaining set. However, if you fall brief of twelve strong reps with 225 pounds, it is able to be which you did no longer permit sufficient relaxation time in advance than doing the set. On the possibility hand, if you have rested a complete three mins earlier than your final set, and you continue to fall brief of your robust rep max of twelve reps, you have got were given handed your capability for the quantity of strong gadgets you may carry out for a muscle organisation. If this occurs, you may want to make changes by using the usage of cutting yet again on the enormous shape of units on the manner to be at entire strength in the direction of your closing set.

Four Types of Sets

All the gadgets that are to be completed for the four phase training system are basically strong devices, but each segment will consist of a first-rate shape of sturdy set. The 4 varieties of devices you'll be doing encompass:

Power warmth up devices

Ascending Single Rep Sets

Mini devices or Half Sets

Full Sets

Since each shape of set corresponds to a superb section of the workout, every type of set may be described at the facet of an intensive rationalization of the 4 stages in the next chapters.

Four Phases Explained

The starting of your workout includes a warmth up this is performed in levels. In the number one phase, you'll be doing electricity heat up devices which encompass severa reps each. In the second section, you'll be doing ascending single reps to your heat up.

Avoid a Warm up That Causes Fatigue

Keep in mind that warmness up gadgets want to be performed to prepare your muscle groups for heavier weights. If you do your warm up units well, your muscle organizations have to revel in energized and have the capability to transport through a complete form of motion without ache for the workout you are doing. When carried out correctly, your warmth up want to maximise your strength degree for heavier lifting. With this in thoughts, in no manner make the mistake of carrying yourself out with heat up devices and compromising your diploma of power while you get to the heavier portion of the workout.

Phase 1: Power Warm up Sets

The exercise starts with or three strength warmth up gadgets in section one. You may be the use of mild weights and will simplest push a 3rd of the manner to a robust rep max for each set. Why no longer push similarly into the set? Because heat up gadgets should not produce fatigue. The concept is to avoid fatigue whilst in spite of the fact that doing plenty of reps as a way to increase blood go along with the glide and viscosity to the operating muscle. This will enhance your flexibility and growth the benefit with which you may flow. Depending at the workout which you pick out out out, phase one will embody one of the warmups which may be listed under:

Chapter 5: Explosive Warm Up Reps

You will decorate in the place of speedy force production if you do your power warm temperature up reps in an explosive, but controlled way. Explosive does no longer suggest careless or injurious. If you want to ease your way into each set with the useful resource of starting with slower reps on the begin of the units, and building as tons as extra explosive reps towards the surrender of the sets, that is flawlessly fantastic. The advantage of lifting forcefully with powerful reps is that it will activate sturdy nerve firing and the use of rapid twitch muscle fibers. This will activate your disturbing device and assist to maximise your energy degree for the rest of your exercise.

Phase 2: Ascending Single Reps

After you do the energy warmness up sets in segment one, you could circulate into segment of your warm up and start doing unmarried reps with heavier weight. Whereas the cause of segment one is to construct explosive strength, the reason of segment is to assemble energy, even on the equal time as warming up. The amount of weight which you use need to growth for every single. Phase will variety in accordance the exercising you pick out. There are 3 versions that correspond to the 3 physical sports as you could see within the following examples:

Phase 2: Ascending Single Reps -- Corresponds to the 8 Set Workout

Set #3: 1 rep: Use a weight that permits 8 strong reps, however high-quality do 1 rep

Set #4: 1 rep: Use a weight that allows 4 strong reps, but only do 1 rep

Set #five: 1 rep: Use your unmarried rep training max weight

Phase 2: Ascending Single Reps -- Corresponds to the 10 Set Workout

Set #4: 1 rep: Use a weight that lets in 12 strong reps, however excellent do 1 rep

Set #5: 1 rep: Use a weight that permits 8 strong reps, but simplest do 1 rep

Set #6: 1 rep: Use a weight that permits 4 strong reps, but simplest do 1 rep

Set #7: 1 rep: Use your single rep education max weight

Phase 2: Ascending Single Reps -- Corresponds to the 7 Set Workout

Set #3: 1 rep: Use a weight that allows 12 robust reps, however nice do 1 rep

Set #4: 1 rep: Use a weight that permits eight robust reps, but best do 1 rep

Set #5: 1 rep: Use a weight that allows four robust reps, but most effective do 1 rep

Warm up has ended When You Reach Your Single Rep Max

Although most of phase two consists of warm temperature up singles that lead up on your single rep training max, the training max is not a warmness up set, even though it is in section for the 8 and ten set workout workouts. You can be pushing on your potential of weight for a single rep at the identical time as though preserving a sturdy lifting motion. This method you ought at the manner to use a smooth nonstop lifting movement without slowing down within the route of the improve, and also you have so you can keep brilliant lifting form.

A Training Effect

When performed well, the 2 section heat up have to do more than to without a doubt prepare your muscle for heavier weights, it will absolutely have a education effect and prompt the strength building procedure thru constructing speedy pressure manufacturing and power into your lifts. If you do your warmth up properly, you need to feel organized to transport at once to the zero.33 and fourth ranges as a way to be stated inside the next section.

A Method Used thru Champions

While the best and comfortable up part of degrees one and two must essentially experience pretty smooth, the workout becomes more difficult while you achieve your schooling max and then head into degrees 3 and four. Phase 3 consists of mini sets or 1/2 of devices, and section 4 includes a entire set. The motive of mini devices and half of devices desires explanation if you need to apprehend how and why to do them.

A Method Used thru Champions: Rethinking a Set

In the past, the maximum vital belief among lifters grow to be that the stop of a set had the most have an impact on on on building strength because it changed into more hard than the sooner a part of the set. In more modern-day instances, many lifters have reversed their thinking about this. With a hint little little bit of concept, it is straightforward to parent out that your first rate energy functionality is at the start of a hard and fast earlier than fatigue has accrued. This being actual, many lifters and coaches started out out to attention on simply doing the number one few reps of a difficult and rapid in which maximum pressure is probably used, and getting rid of the stop of the set earlier than fatigue set in. Stopping a difficult and rapid after best performing some forceful reps, even if a lifter may additionally moreover moreover have the ability to do many more reps, is now a reasonably common method for constructing electricity.

Mini Sets

A complete set calls for which you push on your sturdy rep max. However, if the variety of reps that is used for a complete set is damaged into as a minimum 3 smaller units, the following smaller devices may be known as mini sets. An instance of this will be to take a complete set of twelve reps and smash it into 4 mini units of three reps every. The fashion of reps in a series of mini units need to integrate together to same the same huge fashion of reps as a entire set. In our instance in which one entire set of twelve reps is divided into four mini devices, every mini set consists of three reps, but you could just as without issue use six mini devices of reps, or three mini sets of four reps to acquire at twelve total reps.

Half Sets

A 1/2 set refers to doing half of the sort of reps which you might do for an entire set. For example, a whole set of ten reps may be broken into two half of devices of 5 reps, that can moreover identical ten reps.

Phase three: Half Sets or Mini Sets

Phase 3 is wherein 1/2 of of units are used and you may do barely over a 1/2 of set if you want. You is probably using a weight that lets in eight to 10 strong reps, and do 1/2 devices of 5 reps. You can also choose to do three mini units of three reps, or 5 mini units of reps, but, please apprehend that the more mini gadgets you grow to be doing, the longer your workout is going to take. If you have got were given been to do half of units, then phase 3 have to encompass one of the following options depending on which workout you pick:

Phase 3: Half Sets or Mini Sets According to the eight & 10 Set Workouts

Half Set: 5 reps: Use a weight that permits eight to 10 strong reps, but only do 5 reps.

Half Set: 5 reps: Use a weight that permits 8 to 10 sturdy reps, but handiest do five reps.

Phase three: Half Sets of Mini Sets According to the 7 Set Workout

Set #6: 5 reps: Use a weight that lets in eight to ten sturdy reps, however best do 5 reps.

Phase 4: A Full Set

In section four, you will do your final set. It may be a set in that you push to your strong rep max for twelve to fifteen reps. This is an vital set as it will will allow you to realise whether or not or now not or not you're at complete strength even as you end strolling a muscle organization. If you cannot reap your robust rep max that you could typically do on the identical time as you're at complete energy, then you definitely definately truly are each doing too many gadgets and need to cut back in your workout, or you want to allow more rest time in advance than your last set. Another important thing of the final set is that it serves as a gauge for figuring out whether or not or not you are prepared to function weight for your physical sports. This is probably referred to inside the monetary disaster on "Add Weight at the Right Rate." Make nice you push to your sturdy rep max for twelve to 15 reps on your complete set in section 4. The written a part of section 4 is demonstrated beneath and is the same for the 8 set, 10 set, and 7 set exercising routines.

Phase four: Full Set

Last Set: 12 to fifteen reps: Use a weight that allows a sturdy rep max of 12 to fifteen reps

Precision Training: The Key to Success

Focus on Your Training State

When searching on the four degrees of the exercises, it's critical to understand that wonderful human beings can do the ideal equal exercising in phrases of gadgets, reps, and weight, however regardless of the reality that they are doing the same exercise, one character may be manner off in terms of training to the limit of their capacities, and the alternative character can be right heading in the proper course. The man or woman who is off neglects to train with precision in regard to their sturdy rep max, their unmarried rep education max, and their functionality for strong gadgets. They are definitely looking for to meet a quota of units and reps at the same time as every falling brief, or exceeding their capacities. The awesome person nails it with precision in terms of pushing to their power unique capacities with out exceeding them. The first person believes that in the occasion that they surely do a predetermined variety of gadgets and reps that someone else is using, they have got finished the proper workout, however they'll be incorrect, wrong, incorrect. The 2d individual does the equal workout, but is targeted an extended way extra on undertaking a particular physiological education u . S . A ., in location of doing a required variety of units and reps to reap consequences.

The Phases are Flexible According for your Physical Capacities

The levels of the workout are bendy. The gadgets and reps indexed in every segment aren't supposed to be guidelines that could by no means be adjusted (What I'm about to mention is important, so be cautious to get this aspect). If there may be a rule, it is to teach to the restrict of your power specific capacities without exceeding them, and you may want to add or subtract units within a section to suit your capacities. For instance, you could select the ascending singles reps element from the ten set exercise, and integrate it with truly one 1/2 of set demonstrated in the seven set workout. You can also want to add an additional warm up set, or a further whole set. If these changes, or any modifications, are proper for your training capacities, then cause them to. The crucial idea is to make bigger a physical consciousness of your personal capacities, and to permit that be the final manual for the quantity of devices, reps, and weight to apply.

The Benefit of Variety

Let me furthermore emphasize that every phase consists of various kinds of gadgets to increase one in each of a kind tendencies that combine collectively to assemble electricity. Power heat up units bring together a greater potential for brief pressure production. Ascending single reps construct energy. Mini devices and half gadgets bring together strength, power, and muscle groups. All of the gadgets in tiers one through three are designed to avoid fatigue and to strongly emphasize forceful lifting and most nerve firing.

The entire set in section four differs from the other devices of the workout because it creates extra fatigue. Full gadgets require you to push further into your set with a higher range of reps. The gain to that is that greater reps will stimulate more blood glide to the jogging muscle that would facilitate a pump and increase capillary improvement. Full gadgets may additionally even stimulate the lactate gadget to play a stronger role during exercising a good way to normally will be predisposed to beautify the effects of growth hormone. Growth hormone has an anabolic impact that produces muscle boom.

The bottom line is that masses of various forms of devices are used in the 4 phase education device as every kind of training has its blessings. Once you apprehend a manner to do the 4 levels of the exercising, it's far vital that you recognize while to feature weight in your bodily games. Progressing on the right charge is vital to your achievement.

Add Weight at the Right Rate

Planning Your Progress

In the Planning Progression Table as a way to be furnished at the end of this bankruptcy, you may see how frequently you would need to benefit 5 pounds of power a terrific manner to advantage everywhere from twenty to one hundred pounds of strength over the route of a twelve months. However, the primary prerequisite that want to be finished earlier than inclusive of weight is based totally totally on the use of your single rep training max, and your sturdy rep max (the closing set) as a gauge. When which includes weight, you must although be able to do your unmarried rep schooling max the usage of a strong lifting movement. You ought to additionally be able to do the equal style of sturdy reps in your final set (in phase four) whilst weight is introduced, rather than converting robust reps with inclined reps to attain a preferred rep variety. For instance, we'll take into account that you were doing twelve sturdy reps with the burden you have were given been the use of. You then add 5 kilos and locate which you are pressured to do 11 sturdy reps plus one prone rep at the manner to acquire twelve reps. If this takes place, then you definately aren't prepared to feature weight but. Keep doing twelve reps with the burden you have got been the usage of until you decorate to the issue wherein you can but do twelve strong reps while you upload weight.

Do not resort to doing susceptible reps or a vulnerable lifting movement a good way to function weight. Adding weight and reps isn't the only key to gaining strength. Training at thresholds is the number one key to gaining energy because it forces your electricity precise capacities to growth. Once your electricity precise capacities have improved, only then does including weight turn out to be a key, as it reasons you to teach at your complete capacities again.

The Adaptation Period

The amount of time that it takes for the weights to come to be easy sufficient to lift so that you can add weight is called an version period. If you're progressing efficiently, every model duration need to experience much like the closing version period in phrases of effort. They continually start out a piece harder when weight is brought and get much less hard until you add weight another time. You can start a brand new version length at the same time as you may add weight without exceeding your capability for a robust lifting movement whilst doing all your unmarried rep max, or compromising to your sturdy rep max.

Progressing at a Realistic Rate

You must be sensible whilst making plans your improvement. Although people have a propensity to gain power at high-quality prices, a vast guideline is that novices regularly discover it much less complicated to gain energy at a faster charge; in particular inside the case of a person who has the herbal capability to advantage energy fast. A amateur who is an easy gainer may be capable of upload five pounds to a boost every week or two when they start training. However, progress tends to gradual down for maximum people inside 4 to six months, at which component it will be greater not unusual to characteristic weight each three or four weeks. Within a year of schooling, it'll possibly be regular to want an version duration of five to twelve weeks in advance than consisting of 5 pounds.

A newbie can also benefit 100 or more pounds of energy in a 12 months for carrying events like the squat and deadlift. Someone who already has six months of education at the back of them also can control a power gain of thirty to sixty kilos during the following twelve months. A twenty to thirty pound strength advantage over the path of a three hundred and sixty 5 days for each essential exercise would be commendable for someone who has been education for severa years. Generally, the longer you educate, the greater hard it is to gain.

Progress at Your Own Pace

You may additionally stand up to advantage slower, or you could display as a lot as gain faster than the hints that I surely have supplied. They are definitely not unusual tendencies in place of guidelines that take a look at in all instances. The important factor is to characteristic weight consistent with the fee at which your body is responding. It's furthermore crucial to don't forget that when you have been education for a 12 months or greater, you could observe that your development has slowed down.

Chapter 6: Steps For Safe And Effective Training

At this factor, you should have sufficient data to training session the usage of the four phase training device. Remember to choose only a few crucial compound bodily sports that cover the yet again, chest, and leg/glute muscle groups. Also recollect to teach 3 to six times consistent with week. If you are just beginning out training for the primary time, I recommend schooling on 3 nonconsecutive days in keeping with week. Once you start schooling, you could display your body and add on schooling days if you revel in like you are recovering with out issues among exercise exercises.

As you start the four section training device, truely taken into consideration one in all your first goals have to be to get a feel for your strength degree. You will need to check till you find out the right amount of weight in courting to the amount of robust reps which can be particular for each set. Using the proper quantity of weight for every set is a huge key to long time education fulfillment.

If you're Just Beginning to Work out

If you are new to weight schooling, start out with slight weights which can be clean to raise on your first week of schooling and art work on workout shape earlier than lifting any heavy weights. In reality, I endorse absolutely doing the number one three units of the exercising in phase one in case you are new to weight schooling. Beginners is probably realistic to characteristic right now to their exercising grade by grade over a duration of at least 5 weeks in step with the subsequent plan.

Week 1 Workout

Week 2 Workout

Week 3 Workout

Week 4

Proceed As You Feel Ready

If at any thing to your training, your muscular tissues or joints sense uncomfortable, prone, sore, or liable to harm, back off as hundreds as crucial thru lowering the amount of weight and gadgets you are the use of. Make certain to education consultation at a level of training strain that your frame is cushty with. If a brilliant exercising does now not feel snug, both back down to a lighter weight and great your exercise shape earlier than little by little such as weight over again, or find a completely specific exercising for the identical muscle group that your body is snug with. Do no longer education consultation with weights if you are injured. Only resume schooling with mild weights after an harm in case your body is cushty with mild weights, and regularly construct to heavier weights so long as you stay pain unfastened.

Ready for a Full Workout

If you want to maintain repeating the exercise indexed for week 4 for numerous weeks to experience organized for a whole exercising and a schooling max, don't hesitate to gain this. Assuming you're prepared for an entire exercising, the 3 exercises are indexed all all once more in the subsequent segment. Choose a whole exercise collectively with both 8 gadgets, 10 sets, or 7 units consistent with exercise consistent with your functionality to complete a workout at whole power. If the exercise physical activities don't wholesome your workload functionality, instructions for the manner to make adjustments to the exercising sporting events are cited afterwards.

Choosing Your Workout

eight Sets steady with Exercise Workout: 30 to forty Minutes

Instructions: Do three essential compound bodily video games collectively with:

1. A squat or deadlift exercise for leg/glute muscle groups

2. A pressing exercise for chest, triceps, and deltoid muscle mass

three. A pulling exercising for back, biceps and rear deltoid muscle groups

Use the following sets, reps, and weight for every exercise:

Phase 1: Power Warm up Sets

Set #1: 10 reps: Use a weight that allows 30 sturdy reps, however only do 10 reps

Set #2: 6 reps: Use a weight that permits 18 robust reps, but handiest do 6 reps

Phase 2: Ascending Single Reps

Set #3: 1 rep: Use a weight that allows eight sturdy reps, but pleasant do 1 rep

Set #4: 1 rep: Use a weight that lets in 4 strong reps, but simplest do 1 rep

Set #five: 1 rep: Use your single rep training max weight

Phase three: Half Sets or Mini Sets

Set #6: five reps: Use a weight that allows eight to ten robust reps, but most effective do 5 reps.

Set #7: five reps: Use a weight that allows eight to ten robust reps, but best do 5 reps.

Phase four: Full Sets

Set #eight: 12-15 reps: Use weight that lets in a robust rep max of 12 to 15 reps.

Training Frequency and rest among Sets

-Do the 8 set workout three to 6 times consistent with week

-Rest 30 to 45 seconds among gadgets 1-4

-Rest 90 seconds before doing set 5, 6, and seven

-Rest 2 to three minutes earlier than doing set eight

Please Note: The term sturdy reps and robust rep max are described in economic wreck 7, and the term unmarried rep schooling max is defined in financial disaster 8.

Click right right right here for a downloadable pdf version of the eight set exercise

10 Sets regular with Exercise Workout: 36 to 45 Minutes

Instructions: Do 3 essential compound sports activities activities which encompass:

1. A squat or deadlift exercise for leg/glute muscle groups

2. A urgent exercising for chest, triceps, and deltoid muscle tissue

3. A pulling exercising for lower once more, biceps and rear deltoid muscle tissues

Use the subsequent gadgets, reps, and weight for every workout:

Phase 1: Power Warm up Sets

Set #1: 10 reps: Use a weight that allows 30 sturdy reps, but satisfactory do 10 reps

Set # 2: eight reps: Use a weight that allows 24 strong reps, however most effective do 8 reps.

63

Set #3: 6 reps: Use a weight that lets in 18 strong reps, but simplest do 6 reps

Phase 2: Ascending Single Reps

Set #four: 1 rep: Use a weight that allows 12 sturdy reps, but most effective do 1 rep

Set #5: 1 rep: Use a weight that lets in 8 robust reps, but first-class do 1 rep

Set #6: 1 rep: Use a weight that lets in four robust reps, however exceptional do 1 rep

Set #7: 1 rep: Use your unmarried rep schooling max weight

Phase 3: Half Sets or Mini Sets

Set #8: five reps: Use a weight that allows eight to ten strong reps, but excellent do 5 reps.

Set #nine: five reps: Use a weight that allows 8 to ten robust reps, but only do 5 reps.

Phase four: Full Sets

Set #10: 12-15 reps: Use weight that allows a robust rep max of 12 to fifteen reps.

Training Frequency and rest among Sets

-Do the 10 set workout three to 6 instances in step with week

-Rest 30 to 45 seconds among devices 1-6

-Rest 90 seconds earlier than doing set 7, 8, and nine

-Rest 2 to 3 minutes in advance than doing set 10

Please Note: The time period strong reps and sturdy rep max are defined in bankruptcy 7, and the term unmarried rep schooling max is defined in monetary catastrophe eight.

Click proper right here for a printable pdf model of the ten Set exercise

7 Sets constant with Exercise Workout: 25 to 35 Minutes

Instructions: Do 3 simple compound sports sports which includes:

1. A squat or deadlift workout for leg/glute muscle organizations

2. A urgent workout for chest, triceps, and deltoid muscle tissues

3. A pulling exercising for yet again, biceps and rear deltoid muscle mass

Use the subsequent gadgets, reps, and weight for every exercise:

Phase 1: Power Warm up Sets

Set #1: 10 reps: Use a weight that allows 30 strong reps, however amazing do 10 reps

Set #2: 6 reps: Use a weight that permits 18 sturdy reps, but best do 6 reps

Phase 2: Ascending Single Reps

Set #three: 1 rep: Use a weight that permits 12 robust reps, but best do 1 rep

Set #four: 1 rep: Use a weight that permits 8 strong reps, but high-quality do 1 rep

Set #5: 1 rep: Use a weight that permits four strong reps, but best do 1 rep

Phase 3: Half Sets or Mini Sets

Set #6: five reps: Use a weight that allows eight to ten robust reps, however most effective do five reps.

Phase 4: Full Sets

Set #7: 12-15 reps: Use weight that lets in a sturdy rep max of 12 to fifteen reps.

Training Frequency and relaxation among Sets

-Do the 7 set workout three to 6 times consistent with week

-Rest 30 to forty five seconds among devices 1-5

-Rest 90 seconds before doing gadgets 6

-Rest 2 to a few minutes earlier than doing set 7

Please Note: The time period sturdy reps and robust rep max are described in financial ruin

7, and the time period single rep education max is defined in bankruptcy 8.

Click here for a printable pdf version of the 7 set exercise

Adjustments Part 1: Three Phases in line with Workout

You may additionally discover that in conjunction with all four ranges in every exercise is surely too much. One manner to remedy that is with the aid of the usage of in truth doing three ranges in keeping with exercising. This can be completed primarily based totally on the 8 set, ten set, or seven set physical activities. Phase 1 is a warmth up that want to be protected in each workout, which gives you three possible combos for three phase wearing activities. Ideally, you'll do every exercising on separate days until you have got finished all three workout routines once, then you definately would possibly begin over with the number one workout over again. The following bodily games are examples of three viable combinations of three section workout exercises based totally totally on the 10 set exercise.

Three Phase Workout: Phases 1, 2 and three

Instructions: Do three smooth compound sports sports which incorporates:

1. A squat or deadlift workout for leg/glute muscles

2. A urgent workout for chest, triceps, and deltoid muscle corporations

3. A pulling exercising for again, biceps and rear deltoid muscular tissues

Use the following gadgets, reps, and weight for every workout:

Phase 1: Power Warm up Sets

Set #1: 10 reps: Use a weight that lets in 30 strong reps, but fine do 10 reps

Set # 2: 8 reps: Use a weight that allows 24 strong reps, however nice do 8 reps.

Set #three: 6 reps: Use a weight that permits 18 robust reps, but most effective do 6 reps

Phase 2: Ascending Single Reps

Set #four: 1 rep: Use a weight that lets in 12 strong reps, but satisfactory do 1 rep

Set #5: 1 rep: Use a weight that allows 8 robust reps, however only do 1 rep

Set #6: 1 rep: Use a weight that allows 4 robust reps, however exceptional do 1 rep

Set #7: 1 rep: Use your single rep training max weight

Phase three: Half Sets or Mini Sets

Set #8: 5 reps: Use a weight that lets in 8 to ten strong reps, but extremely good do 5 reps.

Set #nine: 5 reps: Use a weight that allows 8 to ten sturdy reps, but most effective do five reps.

Training Frequency and relaxation among Sets

-Workout three to 6 instances in line with week

-Rest 30 to forty five seconds between gadgets 1-7

-Rest ninety seconds earlier than doing set 8 & nine

Please Note: The time period robust reps and sturdy rep max are defined in chapter 7, and the term single rep schooling max is described in financial spoil 8.

Three Phase Workout: Phases 1, 2 and 4

Instructions: Do 3 easy compound sporting sports activities consisting of:

1. A squat or deadlift exercising for leg/glute muscle groups

2. A pressing workout for chest, triceps, and deltoid muscle groups

three. A pulling exercising for over again, biceps and rear deltoid muscle tissues

Use the subsequent gadgets, reps, and weight for each exercising:

Phase 1: Power Warm up Sets

Set #1: 10 reps: Use a weight that permits 30 robust reps, but excellent do 10 reps

Set # 2: 8 reps: Use a weight that lets in 24 robust reps, but exquisite do 8 reps.

Set #3: 6 reps: Use a weight that allows 18 sturdy reps, however only do 6 reps

Phase 2: Ascending Single Reps

Set #4: 1 rep: Use a weight that permits 12 sturdy reps, but handiest do 1 rep

Set #5: 1 rep: Use a weight that lets in 8 sturdy reps, however pleasant do 1 rep

Set #6: 1 rep: Use a weight that permits 4 sturdy reps, but quality do 1 rep

Set #7: 1 rep: Use your unmarried rep training max weight

Phase four: Full Sets

Set #eight: 12-15 reps: Use weight that lets in a sturdy rep max of 12 to 15 reps.

Training Frequency and rest between Sets

-Workout 3 to 6 instances consistent with week

-Rest 30 to 45 seconds among devices 1-7

-Rest 2 minutes earlier than doing set 8

Please Note: The term sturdy reps and sturdy rep max are described in financial ruin 7, and the time period single rep training max is defined in financial ruin 8.

Three Phase Workout: Phases 1, 3 and 4

Instructions: Do three easy compound carrying activities together with:

1. A squat or deadlift workout for leg/glute muscle organizations

2. A urgent workout for chest, triceps, and deltoid muscular tissues

3. A pulling workout for again, biceps and rear deltoid muscle tissues

Use the subsequent sets, reps, and weight for every exercise:

Phase 1: Power Warm up Sets

Set #1: 10 reps: Use a weight that permits 30 sturdy reps, however simplest do 10 reps

Set # 2: 8 reps: Use a weight that allows 24 sturdy reps, however best do 8 reps.

Set #3: 6 reps: Use a weight that allows 18 sturdy reps, however only do 6 reps

Phase 3: Half Sets or Mini Sets

Set #4: five reps: Use a weight that allows eight to 10 strong reps, however only do five reps.

Set #five: five reps: Use a weight that lets in eight to 10 sturdy reps, but incredible do five reps.

Phase four: Full Sets

Set #6: 12-15 reps: Use weight that lets in a sturdy rep max of 12 to fifteen reps.

Training Frequency and rest among Sets

-Do the ten set workout three to six times in line with week

-Rest 30 to forty five seconds among gadgets 1-three

-Rest 90 seconds earlier than doing set four and ninety seconds earlier than doing set 5

-Rest 2 to three minutes in advance than doing set 6

Please Note: The time period strong reps and robust rep max are described in monetary damage 7, and the time period single rep education max is described in financial ruin eight.

Adjustments Part 2: Two Exercises in line with Workout

Another smooth adjustment in case you pick out shorter exercise workout routines is to choose out either the 7 set, 8 set, or 10 set exercise, however simplest do bodily video games on your sporting activities in desire to 3 bodily video games. If you cut lower back to two fantastic bodily video games every exercise, you could cowl your chest, back, and leg/glute muscle companies two times out of each three workouts.

Chapter 7: Switching Between Physical Games

If you are searching out processes to complete your physical activities quicker, otherwise you need greater cardiovascular benefit out of your sports activities, you may switch from side to side among carrying sports activities at strategic factors in your exercises. Phase three and segment 4 require extra relaxation time amongst gadgets. Instead of truely sitting there or doing now not anything amongst sets, you may do a extraordinary workout at the identical time as nevertheless allowing the muscle organisation which you had been on foot to recover. An instance will assist to make clean how this can be done.

If you're beginning your exercise with the bench press for the eight set exercising, you can preserve through strength warmth up sets, plus the ascending unmarried reps, and the first half of of set with very little relaxation among gadgets. However, you could need time for your chest and triceps to

77

get higher amongst half devices, so you can begin in your energy warmth up phase for squats via using doing warmness up devices. After completing the ones heat up gadgets, skip decrease lower back to the bench press and do your final half of of set in segment three. Return to the squat and do your ascending unmarried reps. When you end your ascending single reps for the squat, you may do your remaining set of bench press in which you push to your strong rep max. You can comprise the strength warmness up for seated pulley rows amongst half of of sets of the squat, and art work in your ascending single reps for seated pulley rows earlier than doing the remaining complete set of squats. If you want the mission of getting thru a exercise quicker with a extra impact in your cardiovascular device, switching amongst bodily sports at the right elements to your exercise will help you.

Adjustments Part four: What in case you Need to do More?

If you're blessed with the capacity to stay at entire power for a massive form of gadgets, you may find out that you could upload right away to the 10 set workout. You can accomplish this through manner of truly along side on more devices to the phase (or levels) of your preference. Make positive you understand the amount of weight you could use for a sturdy rep max of twelve reps and keep to use your final set as a gauge as to whether or now not or no longer you are at complete energy. If you strive inclusive of extra devices onto your exercising and discover that you fall brief of twelve sturdy reps that you could typically do with the weight you've got got got been the use of in your last set, you are better off now not inclusive of any extra devices. Avoid susceptible education, and high-quality upload on greater gadgets if you can do so whilst education at entire electricity

A Strength Building Diet

While you don't need a fancy food plan to boom your power, you do need a balanced healthy eating plan this is enough to fulfill your nutritional needs. Without enough of the proper nutrients, you could discover that even the satisfactory training techniques purpose nowhere in terms of electricity earnings. To insure that this doesn't take area, there a severa elements to preserve in thoughts in regard setting up a food regimen for you to supplement your sporting events.

Calories

It can be very hard to advantage electricity if you are not eating enough. Strength education will stimulate your muscle tissues to utilize incoming nutrients, but your frame cannot make use of vitamins that aren't to be had if you are not eating sufficient. Since people can vary substantially in regard to their metabolic charge and the quantity of bodily hobby that they may be engaged in at some point of a mean day, it is difficult to country a particular quantity of power this is useful for every body. Not absolutely everyone can also preference to advantage weight whilst training for energy. Most parents which might be schooling for electricity don't mind putting on more muscle. If you preference to boom your lean body weight, I suggest increasing your caloric consumption to advantage a chunk at a time. A pound of muscle consistent with week is a completely fast price of muscle benefit. A pound every weeks is excellent, and a pound of muscle every month might be pretty commendable if it's miles finished for severa years.

How Many Meals?

People have gained muscle and strength at the same time as consuming anywhere from to six food consistent with day. Nonetheless, I propose ingesting breakfast, lunch and dinner at the least. Even greater first-rate than 3 food consistent with day is to devour 3 meals with a mid-morning protein snack in amongst breakfast and lunch, and each different mid-afternoon protein snack among lunch and dinner. Eating the proper meals in the form of not unusual meals is a manner to keep your blood sugar degree balanced. This will in turn alter your insulin stage to growth your capacity to benefit muscle and decrease the tendency to advantage fat. In order to benefit strength and muscle, it is also critical to bear in mind what additives you're consuming to gain a balanced weight loss plan.

Carbohydrates, Protein, Fats

Carbohydrates, proteins, and fats are all an vital part of a balanced eating regimen. Overemphasizing, or underemphasizing any of these 3 essential sorts of nutrients may be bad. I'm now not going to make it a rule, but a stylish guiding precept for balance between carbohydrates, proteins, and fats, is to gain forty% of your calories from carbohydrates, 30% of your energy from protein, and 30%

from fat. You might not typically flawlessly acquire this balance, but if you are quite near, you may insure which you have grow to be enough electricity from every form of food.

Quality Food

The maximum extraordinary protein for building muscle is whey protein. Lean meats, eggs, and dairy products (that are not excessively immoderate in brought sugar) also are proper resources of protein.

Complex carbohydrates which consist of easy fruits, vegetables, and entire grains are the basis for excessive terrific carbohydrates. Sugar, immoderate fructose corn syrup, and white flour are smooth carbs that have a propensity to over-growth your blood sugar stage. If you need to maintain your blood sugar level beneath manipulate and keep away from gaining fats, it is best to keep away from ingredients that incorporate smooth carbs.

Fats also are a vital part of your food regimen, but I propose averting trans-fat, this is frequently placed in fried food and commercially prepared baked items. If you test the nutrients label at the applications, trans-fats usually suggests up at the label as "partially hydrogenated oils." The hydrogenation approach can adjust the fat molecules in a way that makes it much less healthful. If for a few purpose you need to function fat to your weight loss plan because it basically includes low fats meals, I recommend coconut oil.

Food Compatibility

One aspect to don't forget is whether or not or no longer the food you are eating is properly matched collectively together with your private frame shape. Some humans can devour almost something with none terrible consequences, even as other human beings revel in bad thing outcomes from sure ingredients. No depend how wholesome a food is declared to be, if it has a terrible impact for your stomach, or motives some one-of-a-type facet effect, dispose of it from your food regimen, or reduce how masses of it you eat until the difficulty results go away. Eat materials which might be clean an awesome way to digest and function a extremely good impact on the manner you experience.

Diet is Important but....

A proper basic diet plan is an crucial a part of gaining power, but diet plan isn't always so vital that you need to spend loads of extra greenbacks consistent with three hundred and sixty 5 days to construct muscle and get stronger. I'm not in opposition to using nutritional nutritional supplements that provide you with effects, and I have no hassle recommending that you use a whey protein complement to insure that your protein intake is ideal enough, but the sports activities sports vitamins industry has made it smooth that allows you to lay our a fortune on supplements, masses of which are not critical to your success. I accept as true with the fine vitamins comes from a remarkable weight loss plan, so start with that. The right exercise will play a huge function in inflicting your body to utilize the nutrients from an amazing eating regimen, so my recommendation is to depend with the aid of and huge upon appropriate meals and suitable exercise routines for achievement, in area of a magic pill or supplement.

Chapter 8: The Benefit Of Precise Training

You Have the Secrets to Keep on Gaining Strength

You can discover a whole lot of sports activities as a way to wonder your frame into short time period electricity profits, but they suddenly surrender strolling. Beware of falling in love with idea of locating a brief repair for gaining energy or questioning which you ought to revel in speedy income all of the time. You can be capable of gain strength short when you first begin to exercising, however it takes sound training mixed with time and consistency in case you need to maximize your strength.

If you practice the thoughts which is probably provided in this e-book, you may acquire the advantages of specific schooling. Precise schooling manner education proper as much as the capacities of your single rep schooling max, your strong rep max, and your functionality for doing strong units. This is the secret to getting stronger, and stronger, and stronger; prolonged past the component in which wonderful people get caught. Train constantly, train clever, and you may maximize your electricity. I need you an entire lot success and the wonderful of schooling.

Exercise Guide

Proceed to the Exercise Guide in the subsequent section for certain instructions on a way to do wearing sports activities.

Squats

Muscles of emphasis: Quadriceps, hamstrings, gluteus, lower once more

Exercise Instructions

1. In order to apply sufficient weight for the barbell squat, you need a squat rack that already has weight located simply below shoulder degree.

2. Place the bar throughout the decrease returned of your shoulders and set up in a standing position with toes a chunk wider than shoulder width.

three. Keeping your back instantly, squat down until your thighs are parallel with the floor and move lower back to a status function. Repeat the exercise motion till the preferred quantity of repetitions has been completed.

Tips and Considerations

The ratio the diverse length of your top body and the duration of your legs, plus the ratio amongst your pinnacle leg and decrease leg may additionally have a large impact on how you squat. A person who has an prolonged top frame and quick legs, and has shorter pinnacle legs than lower legs, should have a miles simpler time squatting in an upright function than a person who possesses lengthy legs, a short better frame, and a long better leg. The person with lengthy legs and a short pinnacle body will want to bend over loads more while moreover permitting their inside the lower back of to paste out inside the again of them greater so as to hold their stability. A man or woman with very lengthy legs may find out that a large stance is the best way to hold a fairly upright characteristic with their higher body even as squatting. Each person ought to have to test to discover a manner of squatting that is comfortable for them. If squatting seems very awkward for you, you can need to check yourself in a reflect or get assist from a lifter, or a train who is aware your frame structure and personal dreams.

Deadlifts

Muscles of Emphasis: Thighs, Gluteus and Back

Exercise Instructions:

1. Stand simply in the back of a barbell with ft a touch a awesome deal a great deal less than shoulder width apart. Sit over again on the

identical time as bending over at the waist and keeping your once more without delay. As you sit down decrease again and bend over on the waist, obtain down with every arms to understand the bar.

2. Grasp the bar together together with your fingers approximately shoulder width aside the use of an overhand grip.

3. From the start function, straighten your legs and better frame into a standing function with the bar placing down in the front of your thighs. Do your first-class to preserve your shins perpendicular to the ground during the carry.

4. Carefully lower bar and repeat the exercising until the specific quantity of repetitions has been finished.

Variations:

1. Many humans choose the usage of an overhand grip with one hand and an underhand grip with the opportunity hand at the same time as doing the useless deliver.

2. If you don't have a squat rack, this workout can be accomplished going proper into a complete squat feature to start the useless carry, after which lifting the bar into a standing function. Use a far wider stance via putting your toes slightly wider than shoulder width apart in case you pick out out this method.

3. The sumo useless boom is done in a more upright characteristic with a massive stance and ft mentioned. This is a outstanding model for human beings with longer legs.

Leg Press

Muscles of Emphasis: Quadriceps, Hamstrings, Glutes

Exercise Instructions:

1. Sit in a leg press collectively collectively together with your with you inside the lower back of firmly on the seat and your again centered flat in opposition to the once more rest.

2. Place your ft approximately twelve to eighteen inches apart in competition to the foot platform. The   in addition up you location your toes on the foot platform, the greater it has a tendency to paintings the glute muscle mass of your behind along side the again of your thighs (your hamstrings). The further down you vicinity your ft at the foot platform, the plenty lots less it will art work your glutes and hamstrings, at the same time as using the quadriceps (the front of the thighs) to enhance the burden.

three. Many leg press machines have a protection bar that holds the weights in region. This calls for that you draw close the handles to the safety bar which can be typically placed down via way of the component of your hips. You want to then make bigger your legs right right into a without delay characteristic and rotate the protection bar handles outward.

four. Once you have got prolonged your legs right into a without delay function, lower the weight till your legs are bent at a ninety diploma attitude to installation a starting function. From the start position, growth your legs toward the load until they are directly, then cross back to the start feature. Repeat till you attain the popular huge form of repetitions.

5. Finish collectively together with your legs directly for your final repetition, then maintain close the handles to the safety bar and rotate them lower back up into the begin role. Carefully lower the weights till they are caught via the usage of the protection bar.

Bent Over Barbell Rows

Muscles of Emphasis: Back, Biceps, and Rear Deltoids

Chapter 9: Seated Pulley Rows

Muscles of Emphasis: Back, Biceps, and Rear Deltoids

Exercise Instructions

1. Not all tool for seated pulley rows is the same. The important idea is to face a pulley tool and sit down down down close to sufficient to comprehend the address (preferably a v-bar deal with) at the surrender of the pulley.

2. Legs need to be slightly bent and positioned ahead in the front of the body with the toes placed ahead at the foot platform or crossbar if it is available at the pulley tool.

three. Make effective your top body is located upright with the again right away and chest immoderate.

four. Reach ahead with each arms to recognize the take care of at the cease of the pulley.

five. Pull the address in the direction of your body till it touches the higher stomach location.

6. Squeeze your shoulder blades together as you pull the address into your frame.

7. Lower the load with the beneficial useful resource of returning your hands and fingers to the beginning characteristic inside the the front of your frame.

eight. Repeat pulling the manipulate into your frame and returning it to the starting characteristic for the favored type of repetitions.

Lat Pulldowns

Muscles of Emphasis: Back, Biceps, and rear Deltoids

Exercise Instructions:

1. Sit down on a lat pull seat and reap up with every hands and use a substantial grip to recognize the lat pull bar.

2. While retaining your chest excessive and frame robust, pull the bar down until it touches the middle of your chest.

three. Carefully straighten your fingers again to the start characteristic. Repeat the workout movement until the favored quantity of repetitions were finished.

4. Do no longer jerk again on the identical time as lifting, and do not spherical your decrease back. Your chest need to be held immoderate in order to prevent this.

Variations

Lat pull downs can be achieved with a slender grip. There also are bars or handles that can help you use a narrower grip if you want to placed greater emphasis at the lower lat and middle of the decrease once more in case you squeeze your shoulder blades due to the truth the bar is touching your chest.

Pull-Ups

Muscles of Emphasis: Back, Biceps, and rear Deltoids

Exercise Instructions:

1. Use an overhand grip, or fingers going through every different grip to understand a pull-up bar or pull-up handles.

2. Let your body draw near at arm's length right away down from the bar.

3. Pull your frame without delay up as a minimum till your chin is despite the bar. As you enhance, strive pull up higher until your colour bone or better chest is even with the bar.

4. Keep you again immediately or barely arched as you pull so you can contract your once more muscle mass.

five. Lower your self lower lower back to arm's duration function and repeat pulling yourself up for the popular variety of repetition.

Variations

You can variety the width of your grip and use an underhand grip in case you select.

Bench Press

Emphasis: Chest (Pectoral) Muscles, Triceps, and the the front Deltoids

Exercise Instructions:

1. Position yourself for your once more on a bench press bench.

2. Use an overhand grip to recognize the bar collectively with your arms a hint wider than shoulder width aside.

3. Take the barbell this is on the bench press rack and push it as tons as arm's period above your chest.

4. Carefully decrease the bar down till it is touching your lower chest.

5. Push the bar directly as a good deal as arm's duration.

6. Repeat until you attain the popular range of reps and thoroughly positioned the bar again at the bench press rack that helps the barbell.

Variations

1. A wider grip with elbows significant to the side for the duration of the boom will emphasize the outer chest muscle corporations. Caution, a huge grip with elbows great to the aspect can be traumatic to the shoulder joint if executed too frequently or with weights which may be too heavy.

2. A near grip will emphasize the triceps muscle tissues. Keeping the elbows in close to the frame will emphasize the internal triceps on the another time or your hands and the the front deltoid muscle organizations of the

shoulders. Flaring the elbows out to the aspect at the same time as using a close grip will emphasize the outer triceps muscular tissues of the arms.

3. Dumbbells moreover may be used rather than a barbell as a bench press version.

Incline Press

Muscles of Emphasis: Upper Chest (Pectoral) Muscles, Triceps, and Deltoids

Exercise Instructions

1. Position yourself for your lower again on an incline bench.

2. Use an overhand grip to understand the bar with your hands a hint wider than shoulder width aside.

3. Take the barbell this is at the incline rack and push it as a lot as arm's period above your face.

four. Carefully decrease the bar down until it is touching your higher chest.

five. Push the bar straight away as a splendid deal as arm's duration.

6. Repeat until you obtain the desired extensive type of reps and carefully located the bar decrease lower again at the rack that helps the barbell.

Variations

A wider grip with elbows large to the thing sooner or later of the raise will emphasize the outer muscle groups of your higher chest. A grip with arms closer together will emphasize the the the front deltoid of the shoulders and triceps located on the again of the fingers. Dumbbells additionally can be used in preference to a barbell as an incline press model.

Shoulder Press

Emphasis: Deltoid Muscles of the Shoulders, Triceps, and Upper Back Muscles

Exercise Instructions:

1. Use an overhand grip to realise a barbell a piece wider than shoulder width aside.

2. Sit down on the give up of a bench with the barbell held truly below your chin.

3. Push the barbell immediately up until your arms are absolutely extended over your head.

4. Carefully, (keep away from reducing the barbell right down to your head) lower the barbell lower back into the starting function and repeat the lifting movement till the favored form of repetitions has been finished.

Chapter 10: The History And Basics Of Powerlifting

Since approximately the time our ancestors left within the returned of the caves and started out to create way of life, there has constantly existed the query, "Who is the strongest?" It is a question that has about as many solutions due to the fact the have been folks that try to answer it.

For the historic Greeks and Romans, this query turned into settled via personal trials, as athletes competed in video games of tempo, capability, and strength. These festivals have passed down thru the a long time, and were the muse for our modern-day Olympic video games. Weightlifting emerge as in fact one of the sports contested at the ones first cutting-edge Olympics. Since then, some form of weightlifting has been competed at every Olympics except for 1900, 1908, and 1912.

However, the Olympics by myself were now not the first-rate attempts to settle who became the maximum powerful. Scotland is well-known for its Highland Games, a unique competition in which contestants throw weights that weight upwards of 50 kilos for height, supply massive stones onto structures, and possibly most impressively, reputedly throw wooden-like cabers for distance. The Nordic countries without a doubt have a their private precise strength competitions, which

This variety of styles triggered a plethora of education, and hundreds debate (every so often pleasant, from time to time not plenty). Even inside the Olympics, early at the sports contested could range from Olympiad to Olympiad. By 1928 however, Olympic weightlifting had settled into 3 lifts: the clean and jerk, the take hold of, and the smooth and press (the overhead press become removed inside the early 1972s from Olympic competition), all using the acquainted Olympic fashion barbell and plates.

An offspring of Olympic lifting, powerlifting changed into born from athletes who loved the blessings and the texture of weight schooling, however did now not have each the choice, the need, or the frame kind to become international splendor within the Olympic lifts. Starting in the early 1950's as "abnormal enhance" opposition, powerlifting shared as severa and wooly a beyond because it's Olympic cousin, till within the mid 1960's settling upon the current format of opposition the usage of the squat, the bench press, and the deadlift.

This standardization turn out to be fueled with the aid of way of manner of the powerful hobby of the Amateur Athletic Union, or AAU. Responsible for nearly maximum sports in the United States, the AAU positioned powerlifting beneath the identical magnificence in its form as Olympic lifting and bodybuilding, and for years powerlifting struggled in the shadows of its extra famous and politically connected cousins. Eventually even though, powerlifting break up off from the AAU, with a plethora of federations and organizations retaining their very own competitions. Without Olympic popularity however, powerlifting by no means advanced the monolithic business enterprise organization of Olympic lifting, however the fact that nowadays the International Powerlifting Federation (IPF) is perhaps the closest on a international full-size scale.

About the time that the AAU's manipulate of powerlifting started out to dissolve, generation commenced to play a issue in powerlifting, because of the reality the primary generation of lifting assist "device" and "exceptional fits" started out to come back lower back again into use inside the early 1980's. These tight suits, designed to assist the body in positive lifts, speedy positioned athletes shattering lengthy repute statistics as squat fits and bench shirts allowed coping with of heavier and heavier weights. With the later emergence of 2d generation multi-ply tools, powerlifters have been lifting weights that at one time seemed no longer possible.

This style toward the usage of increasingly more superior powerlifting suits brought about a backlash, but. The query fast emerged: what have grow to be doing the increase, the athlete or the fit? Eventually, athletes and federations discovered a resurgence in interest in so-called "uncooked" lifting, which receives rid of the use of powerlifting fits. While this has introduced approximately document books for powerlifting often seeming perplexing as "global statistics" existed for first rate federations, weight commands, and device allowances, it additionally has supplied the possibility for all people, irrespective of interest, to locate their location of interest in lifting. Many athletes even compete in a single-of-a-type patterns, performing some meets in device earlier than doing one or raw.

On the other hand, this case leads green oldsters to powerlifting to almost migraine inducing conundrums, as they will be confronted with laundry lists of substances and tools to use. To start powerlifting but, it does now not take masses to begin, specifically if you are truely looking at schooling at the begin. To get started powerlifting, in addition to an awesome fitness center, all an athlete will want to train is:

1. A Powerlifting Belt- Different out of your normal "weightlifting belt" that tapers inside the stomach location, a powerlifting belt is traditionally a consistent 4 inches huge all round, and is typically all leather-based-based. Powerlifting belts are frequently stiffer than ordinary belts, once in a while as an entire lot as 12mm thick. Starting out, a 10mm thick belt will serve all your goals, and is crook in nearly all competitions. When it comes to closure style, at the start skip the lever belts that could frequently want adjusting amongst their use within the squat and the deadlift (and are usually greater expensive as properly), and select out both a unmarried or double prong belt.

2. Shoes- The call of the game in powerlifting shoes is flat, tough, and supportive. Normal strolling shoes and skip jogging footwear may be too gentle of their soles for powerful transfer of strength for squats and deadlifts, and no longer supportive enough. Rolling your ankle to the out of doors at the same time as near maximal weights are for your arms or to your again is a first rate manner to have a totally horrible day. Chuck Taylor All-Stars are a not unusual preferred, as they might serve definitely for all 3 lifts, and are generally cheap as well. Some lifters want to squat in Olympic style lifting shoes, as the improved heel could make it lots less tough to attain proper depth, but such footwear aren't an first rate concept for deadlifts.

3. Clothing- for training, snug non restrictive apparel is all you really want. Many competitive lifters will do their uncooked schooling in as an opportunity general t-shirts and shorts. If you desire to compete, a powerlifting singlet (much like a wrestling singlet) is frequently required, although some

federations have a "learners branch" that lets in using normal t-shirts and shorts or compression shorts. Do now not fear about squat fits and such till you are nicely past the scope of this e-book.

There are many different not unusual accessories that regulate from athlete to athlete. Climber's chalk is often used to keep your grip dry and employer, or for keeping the squat bar in which it is supposed to be at the same time as you are education. Knee sleeves, elbow sleeves, and wrist wraps are also not unusual, no matter the fact that a few federations do no longer permit them in opposition. In any case, those special add-ons are not vital, and its as lots as you as to whether or not or not you need to apply them to your training.

Chapter 11: The Competition Lifts

Modern powerlifting is broken down into 3 particular lifts, contested in a famous order. The first enhance contested may be the squat, observed with the aid of way of the usage of the bench press, observed with the aid of the deadlift. Each athlete can also need to have 3 attempts to elevate as heaps weight as viable one time. If you do not have at the least one a success attempt at each elevate, you could have "bombed out," and in better degree competitions not be allowed to maintain at once to the subsequent convey. More on the necessities and competition layout for every raise within the following chapters.

Each elevate is judged with the aid of the usage of a panel of 3 judges, one within the the the the the front and one on each aspect. Using both lights or flags, they'll signal to the pinnacle determine (the front decide) whether or not or no longer they sense that a boost is ideal growth (white) or no raise (red). It takes whites for a boost to be deemed precise normal, so white flags and one purple flag is still a incredible raise.

Competitions are damaged down into weight education, and regularly moreover into enjoy ranges. Different federations have one among a kind limits for his or her weight lessons, with weigh-ins happening both the morning of or the day before competition. Winners are decided through who has the very incredible favored of their terrific squat, bench, and deadlift, with ties internal a weight beauty broken via the usage of versions in frame weight (lighter lifter getting the benefit).

Regardless of who wins or loses, you can regularly locate at powerlifting competitions a enjoy of camaraderie that is difficult to find out in distinct sports activities competitions. This is regularly because of the fact that, initially, powerlifting is this kind of especially small and regularly misunderstood network in the health world that a sense of togetherness is welcomed. Secondly, nearly unique some of the competitive sports activities sports sports, the "enemy" in powerlifting isn't always the possibility athletes, but as an possibility the enemy is the bar and gravity itself. Every powerlifter, from the maximum modern rookie in their first meet to the location champions, is aware of that there exists a weight that they can't elevate..... But. Instead of pursuing gold medals and titles, the first rate achievement maximum lifters are looking for is a personal file, or PR. Many lifters must rather have a PR than a primary region stop.

In well-known, close to powerlifting education, education may be broken down into sorts. The first shape of education can be called "constructing the convey." In constructing the enhance, you are attempting to reinforce the muscle agencies wanted for the opposition lifts. While this may often be performed by means of manner of education the beautify itself, it isn't always usually so, as frequently adjustments and one among a kind physical sports which might be centered at an athlete's particular prone vicinity of a boost may be focused alternatively. For a brand new powerlifter however, most education at constructing the boom might be a few model similar to the competition increase.

The other form of schooling often utilized by powerlifters can be referred to as "education the boost." While it does not appear so from first look, the competition lifts should have very technical factors to them, and subjects which includes hand placement, foot placement, or frame alignment are vital. A difference as small as an inch may be the difference among a high-quality raise and a no carry. In schooling the convey, lifters are frequently using lighter weights within the competition lifts themselves, training their frame and their muscle memory in order that their approach at the competition platform is as ideal as possible.

Chapter 12: The Squat

The squat has a nicely deserved recognition due to the fact the "King of Lifts." Requiring as lots as 70% of your body to complete, the squat is probable the awesome expressions of decrease body electricity.

The squat is also one of the maximum misunderstood and feared lifts, with ignorant so-called experts advising the whole thing from ditching the squat clearly to shortening the form of movement to ridiculous tiers.

For powerlifting opposition, the basics of the squat are clean. From a standing function, with the bar at some stage in the lower back of the shoulders, the athlete will descend until the fold of the hip (wherein the leg starts offevolved offevolved to bend become impartial from the hip joint) is lower than the pinnacle of the knee, after which actually arise. Pausing isn't always allowed except at the extreme bottom and at the top of the increase.

The instructions for the squat are clean. After ascending the platform, you are each waved beforehand or knowledgeable to begin via the top determine (who offers all commands). Once you've got the burden on your shoulders and are equipped to squat, you will pay interest the command "squat." You then at your discretion start your descent "into the hole," or the bottom function. There isn't always any command when you are in the hollow, you try this at your very personal judgment. Once you've got got completely stood up, you will pay attention the command to "rack." At this detail you could rack the bar again into the hooks of the squat stand, and permit the load off your shoulders.

There are crucial sort of squat stands in use. For IPF and most nearby degree competitions, a substantial set of squat stands are used, while a number of the higher diploma powerlifting gyms and fantastic federations permit the usage of a hydraulic "monolift". With stylish squat stands, the bar ought to be "walked out" of the stand in advance than squatting can be finished. With a monolift, the squatter does not need to step lower again at all earlier than the command to squat is given. This is due to the fact the monolift's hooks can be swung up and out of the way of the lifter.

Before the meet, each lifter ought to tell the scoring table what placing the hooks are to be set at for his or her lifts. It is tremendous to apply a top that is only a few inches beneath in which the bar may be even as you are simply status. There isn't always any use is dropping strength half of-squatting the bar up from the hooks earlier than you may even get the command to squat. At the equal time, if your stands are set too immoderate, clearing the bar from the hooks have to show hard, and clipping a hook at the way out can also need to knock you off balance and screw up your function. A perfect trace for you is at the identical time as in training, decide the height from the ground you want your bar to be. Write it down in a training pocket e-book, so that irrespective of warmup time, availability of the opposition platform, or device used, you can fast get your bar in which you want it to be.

The opposition squat isn't always like a bodybuilding squat in which you need to make your sort of motion as low as possible on the equal time as but accomplishing depth. As such, most powerlifters should have a far wider stance than a bodybuilder or conventional athlete, whose interest in on stressing and constructing muscle as opposed to shifting the maximum weight. Some geared lifters are able to use their squats fits so correctly in this that they nearly contact the sides of a monolift on the identical time as they may be in their stance. This places a large amount of pressure on the hip muscular tissues, and maximum beginning lifters can't address this pressure, nor get to proper intensity in such excessive stances. For a starting athlete, a stance wider than shoulder width but no longer ridiculously large is superb. Find your stance that allow you to hit depth usually with little pain to your hips.

Foot mindset in the squat is likewise important. To keep your outstanding stability, you need to try to hold your feet pointed every ahead or at no more than a 45 degree outward attitude. More than that, and you chance reaching a ballet-like pose which threatens stability with a barbell in your over again.

To do a competition squat from a squat stand, the primary secret is bar placement upon your yet again. Some lifters choose a low bar motion, wherein the bar is located almost upon the shoulder blades. Other lifters pick out a higher bar function, with the bar rested upon the trapezius muscle tissues. Once you find out your preferred placement, the first detail to do is disturbing the decrease back muscles, squeezing them and pinching the shoulder blades together, developing a organisation platform in your bar to rest. Hand placement varies with the aid of the lifter, despite the fact that normally the nearer your fingers are collectively, the tighter the squeezing of the shoulders.

Your head and chest ought to be pushed up and again into the bar. Think of imitating a gorilla, with their chest up and eyes without delay earlier. Unrack the bar via pushing your head and lower back into the bar, the use of as little leg electricity as possible. Step yet again carefully, assuming your foot placement. This want to take no more than three or four steps (suitable lifters can do it in). Fill your torso with as loads air as possible, pushing your stomach button into your belt. You're now equipped to squat.

After getting the squat command, the primary movement should be at your hips. Break on the hips, and push them backwards as you descend underneath manipulate (do NOT jump down, it robs you of strength and locations you susceptible to harm), best bending the knees as little as possible to hit depth. Your shins should continue to be as vertical as possible. A properly photo to use with this is to take into account sitting down on a low chair in the lower back of you. Your chest must live up in a gorilla-like stance, collectively together with your eyes steady on a element degree with you. Once you hit depth, again push your head and once more into the bar, and awareness now not on pressing along with your legs however pushing your hips forward. Don't awareness on pushing your hips up, as this frequently reasons you to bend in advance on the waist, leaving your legs straightened at the same time as your decrease lower again is now bent and assuming volatile quantities of stress. Once you're status another time, anticipate the rack command in advance than you leap forward.

For a beginner, doing competition squats time and again will circulate an prolonged manner to now not actually training the improve however also building the deliver. However, this repeated stress upon the hips and shoulders may be carrying, and most lifters will discover that doing precise lifts can relieve strain, constructing up prone regions, and destroy the monotony. Here are a number of the maximum commonplace "accessory lifts."

1. Narrow stance squats- These take masses of stress off your knees and places it extra on your quads and glutes. Take a shoulder width stance, and squat with a chunk bit extra knee damage and ankle flexion than a opposition squat.

2. Box squats- A staple advocated with the useful resource of the famous Louie Simmons and Westside Barbell, container squats are a tremendous tool for ensuring you're hitting depth. Set the sector at sincerely beneath your favored intensity, and preserve a decent frame. You can both do "contact and bypass" field squats, going up as short as your butt touches the container, or entire take a seat down squats, wherein you settle down more, and want to explode up off the container. The key for protection within the field squat is to transport down slow and underneath control. Do now not slam your butt into the world, except you need a broken tailbone. Also, hold

belly tightness the whole time, to hold the low decrease again stable.

three. Band and Chain Squats- An interesting manner to vary the resistance as you squat, bands and chains have end up increasingly more commonplace even in enterprise gyms. Be conscious however that the pressures and balancing effects of bands and chains can affect your balance and coordination to your competition squat, and do no longer make the ones a weekly staple of your pre-contest education.

Chapter 13: The Bench Press

For Western adult adult adult males, the bench press has taken on an almost iconic popularity. When a stranger strategies someone who appears robust, one of the first questions out of their mouth has a bent to be, "So how a whole lot ya bench?"

The opposition bench press, like the competition squat, tends to have widespread variations amongst it and its bodybuilding version. Again, the aim is to make your range of motion as short as feasible whilst despite the fact that preserving your power.

For a competition bench press, the instructions you will typically listen can be "bypass" to can help you carry the burden out of the racks (this will be completed with a spotter's assist). Once the bar is brought out and steadied over the chest, the judge will command "down." You are to decrease the bar until it touches your chest area. Once the bar is at the chest, and the decide feels there isn't any hazard of bouncing the bar off the chest, the following command can be "press." The bar want to be then pressed upwards till your hands are once more at once. Once without delay, and beneath manage, the top determine will then offer the "rack" command.

There are five important ways to get a no-carry for the bench press. First, as within the squat, is not finishing the boom. Secondly, if a lifter both pauses inside the ascent or presses the bar up erratically. Third, if a lifter's hips leave touch with the bench, or if their feet loses contact with the ground. Fourth, if a lifter descends, presses, or racks earlier than the pinnacle determine's call. Finally, if the bar hits the assist palms of the bench during the enhance.

Key variations between the bodybuilding bench press and the powerlifting bench press begin as quickly as you contact the bench. In a bodybuilding bench, the lower back is stored handiest barely arched, and your fingers are positioned extraordinarily shoulder width aside, with the higher lower again being kept flat on the bench to maximize tension at the pectoral muscle businesses. A powerlifter benches the use of their entire body. To shorten the form of movement, an frequently exaggerated arch to the low lower once more is done, with that arch persevering with through to the shoulder blades. The hands are also located wider, with many lifters attempting as huge a grip as legally allowed (powerlifting bars have hash marks on them, which the hands need to stay internal). In addition, the movement is special, with the elbows tucked in greater to engage your lat muscle mass more to press the bar off your chest.

To set up your bench press, upon sitting at the bench the number one trouble you need to do is arch your once more as hard as you may, even as pinching your shoulder blades together. Keep your chin in your chest, and lay backwards. Once you are down, take a 2nd to re-set up your arch. Some lifters like to use the bar to tug themselves down into an awesome deeper arch. Your ft must be placed in a strong position beneath your hips. Some lifters need to tuck their toes as deep as viable under the bench, however this may translate to a lack of lower frame strength for the boom. A greater favored characteristic is to keep them flat on the floor underneath your knees. Push backwards into the bench at the side of your ft, reinforcing your arch.

Once your arch is powerful, vicinity your palms for your position. If you do no longer have access to a powerlifting bar, use a ordinary bar. The "jewelry" on it are desirable publications. Become normal with which finger you operate to do your opposition lifts, and each time you practice the opposition fashion, use that finger. Experiment to discover which finger allows you the maximum energy with the least amount of infection of the shoulder joint (remarkable sizeable grips can frequently irritate your shoulders, particularly for older athletes).

As with the squat, the bench need to be set simply so on the same time as you unrack, you need to first-class need to reinforce the bar an inch or at maximum. If you need to use a spotter, ensure you and your spotter have easy verbal exchange on this hand off of the bar (nice if you convey your personal spotter). Figure out the way you need to have the bar lifted off, and do it the equal on every occasion. Once you have got got the down command, decrease the bar now not on your chest or your nipple line, but lower. Lifters in bench press shirts will often lower the bar almost to their better stomachs, at the same time as for uncooked lifters the touch factor has a bent to be slightly higher.

Another distinction on the powerlifting bench is your elbow function. While bodybuilders will regularly press with the elbows flared out almost perpendicular to the frame, a powerlifter's elbow may be heaps tighter. This will permit your lat muscle groups to help with powering the body off your chest, as well as guard the sensitive shoulder. Geared lifters also can have extra tucks than raw lifters, to take greater benefit of the stretch and tightness of their blouse. For a beginning uncooked lifter, cause for an elbow to frame attitude of approximately 45 levels.

Once the bar touches the chest, you need to make sure to concentrate for the "press" command. Then explode into the bar, urgent strongly and without problems. This movement have to be accomplished with the try of your whole frame. Press collectively collectively together with your feet in advance, to replace energy in your hips, which transfers in your all over again and lats. This permits launch the bar off of your chest, whilst your chest, triceps and shoulders hold the clicking. When you attain lockout, keep the clicking until you listen the "rack" command.

As with the squat, education the bench press itself will make up the bulk of a newbie's workload, each building the convey and schooling the enhance. However, there are masses of accessory lifts available, used for particular reasons. Here are a number of the most not unusual:

1. Incline and Decline Presses- The flat bench may be hell on your shoulders, specifically as you turn out to be older. A specific manner to alleviate the strain for your shoulder joint whilst but setting quite some stress for your pressing muscle tissues is to apply incline and decline presses. A slight attitude, no more than 10 or 15 ranges, is regularly sufficient to take pressure off the shoulders. Be aware however that doing such sports sports most usually receives rid of using leg pressure and takes faraway from arching, because of the mechanics of most business incline and decline benches.

2. Dumbbell Presses- The lovable detail about dumbbell presses is that they permit you to waft your arms and shoulders thru their natural direction of movement. You can rotate your palms, and without troubles artwork on your tucked elbow function. A

very well-known version intended for working at the triceps is to preserve your fingers managing every exceptional, and the dumbbells very tight in your frame. This locations severa stress on your triceps, and is a extraordinary completing accessory pass.

three. Partial ROM paintings- Some lifters like to get used to ordinary weights via the use of partial variety of movement sporting sports activities. Using both a electricity rack with the pins set at a high excellent top, or forums (normally 2x4s) held in competition to the chest with the resource of a schooling companion, a lifter will use a higher than normal weight, and handiest press thru the shorter variety. While a incredible manner to tax the chest, be careful now not to use this too frequently within the beginning, as your bones and tendons adapt to the stress of powerlifting.

Chapter 14: The Deadlift

A as an alternative vintage pronouncing in the powerlifting global is "the meet does not start until the weights touch the ground." The deadlift is the very last enhance contested in powerlifting, and is likely the oldest exercising in life. For powerlifting, types of deadlift dominate, the conventional and the sumo. The handiest way to inform the difference is leg feature. In a conventional deadlift, the legs and toes are within the fingers, at the equal time as in a sumo deadlift the legs are split sizeable, with the palms placing down many of the legs.

The largest problem in selecting which deadlift style is for use frequently comes all of the manner right down to a rely variety of consolation. The conventional deadlift is extremely good for lifters who've stronger hips and occasional backs, and those who are much much less affected person of their setups. The sumo deadlift favors the ones who've greater leg power, and people who are affected person enough to undergo a

133

extra technical setup. In addition, the truth that sumo deadlifters are frequently using extraordinarily massive stances way that their style of movement is much less than a conventional deadlift. Experiment with every, and pick out out the style which you choose satisfactory.

Another variable in deadlift is hand characteristic. The most common setup for hands is alternating, with one hand palm out even as the other hand has the palm coping with the body. This hand characteristic ensures that the fingers are in their most effective grip configuration. However, if you have had bicep or elbow accidents inside the past, this characteristic can region an entire lot of strain upon the bicep tendon. In that instance, some unique preferred grip is the double overhand grip, with both hands going via the frame. While this function is lots less complicated to advantage, and takes strain off of the biceps, the palms aren't in as strong a function, and the bar may additionally furthermore roll out of the palms.

In opposition, the deadlift is possibly the most effective in terms of instructions. Once at the platform, the athlete will pay attention the command "convey." This is regularly given even in advance than you've got gripped the bar. Once at entire lockout, the head choose will offer the command "down." Common no-enhance mistakes embody not finishing the raise, no longer locking out, pausing or letting the bar descend earlier than locking out, and dropping the bar. Also, hitching the bar up the legs isn't authorized. You ought to show manage of the bar the complete time from gripping to putting right down to get an incredible deliver.

In installing for the traditional deadlift, one of the keys is to take the pressure in your hips and coffee once more, and no longer try and "squat-carry" the weight up. Taking a slender stance (about shoulder width or barely a good deal much less), bend the knees simply sufficient to maintain a flat decrease lower back function to grip the bar. Usually, approximately a ninety diploma bend on the waist is satisfactory, with about a 75 to 90 diploma bend at the knee. Another crucial detail of foot placement is bar function. While closer to the body is proper, too close to and also you waste strive and power getting the bar right. A appropriate trace is to comprehend your arms right away down while you are on your setup stance. The bar must fall naturally into your palms. Stand up, and look down at wherein the bar crosses your toes. Try to collect that function whenever you improve. For a traditional lifter, that is often approximately halfway down your ft, near about wherein most footwear stop lacing near the toes.

Once you've got had been given your grip, pull upwards and slightly backwards, powering via your heels as you pressure to lockout. A key aspect proper right here is to make sure that your knees and hips paintings collectively. If you find that your legs are instantly at the same time as the bar remains under your kneecaps, your legs are straightening out too quick.

For the sumo deadlift, installing vicinity is an lousy lot one-of-a-type than a traditional deliver. Firstly, taking as big a stance as without problems possible is crucial. The ft are frequently splayed outward , generally approximately forty five degrees. Your knees want to additionally be pointing outward, at the side of your groin losing right all the way down to the bar. For people with bad groin flexibility or a facts of hernias, that is glaringly no longer a superb concept. Your pinnacle frame should stay heaps more vertical than a traditional deadlifter, with flawlessly right away top our our bodies being not unusual.

Once down, grip the bar by means of the usage of putting your hands without delay down. This grip may be slightly narrower than a conventional lifter, however ought to but stand up at the knurled components of the bar. The bar is going to be very near your frame, and lots of sumo lifters will in truth scrape their shins on the way up with the bar (some federations even require deadlifters to put on excessive socks for opposition because of this, due to the possiblity of blood at the bar). Once you have a company grip, use your thighs, glutes, and groin to electricity thru your mid-foot, in nearly a "squat-enhance" style.

In education the deadlift, it's far probably the first-class carry in which many powerlifters (except for individuals who are virtually adept at the bring) will no longer use the deadlift itself as the bulk of their education in building the deliver. This is because of the fact that a heavy deadlift exercising places notable portions of strain upon the frame's structures, and might often break the important apprehensive tool for days afterwards, making difficult schooling nearly now not viable. In addition, when you consider that some of the muscle corporations worried inside the deadlift bring over to the squat and squat education, an excessive amount of heavy deadlifting can overstress the frame's recuperative powers.

Because of this, the bulk of maximum deadlift constructing schooling is finished the use of accessory bodily sports activities and variations. The maximum not unusual versions embody:

1. Romanian Deadlifts- This nearly right away legged model of the deadlift locations pretty a few stress on the low decrease again and the hamstrings. As such, now not only is it a terrific building movement for traditional deadlifters, but is likewise a common accent motion for the squat as properly. The loss of leg use in the RDL also manner that a fantastic deal much much less weight may be used. When doing the RDL, a shorter form of motion, from certainly under the kneecaps to lockout, is typically advocated, to avoid undue pressure at the decrease spine.

2. Glute Ham Raises/Reverse Hypers- Technically specific lifts, now not each gymnasium has a GHR bench, so on occasion you want to make do. Both of these can region a super amount of stress on the glutes

and occasional again muscle mass, regardless of simply body weight. To advantage brought benefit to the hamstrings, a GHR bench is important. Checking your ego and mastering a manner to use it's miles a tremendous gain, as even seemingly robust human beings will find doing a proper GHR tough at the start.

three. Rows- While not focused on the hips and espresso again, barbell and dumbbell rowing is vital for building the muscle tissue inside the mid to top lower again, which enables no longer certainly the electricity of the deadlift, but additionally gives the strong basis for the squat and the bench press. Additionally, doing heavy rows with out using wrist straps or special grip assists is a notable way to assemble forearm power for heavy deadlifts.

4. Rack Pulls and Partial ROM Deadlifts- Whether the usage of a power rack or blocks, partial form of movement deadlifts convey maximum of the identical advantages of partial range bench presses stated in advance,

similarly to having masses a lot much less pressure on the worried device. If you discover that you can get the bar off of the ground but have troubles locking out, those lifts are first rate for operating via that sticking element. One factor of warning: in case you are doing rack pulls, controlling the bar onto the rack pins is crucial no longer masses for exercise protection, but because of the truth immoderate losing of the bar can bend both the pins and the deadlift bar. Unless you need to each purchase those in bulk, or are inclined to make a health club proprietor very indignant (no longer a very good idea if the gym proprietor is likewise a powerlifter), manage the bar right all the way down to the pins.

Chapter 15: The Program And A Sample Training Cycle

The key for maximum starting powerlifters is to no longer soar too deep into the water in the starting. It takes years for a person's frame to adapt to the depth of training that a immoderate diploma powerlifter places it thru. Getting silly and letting enthusiasm outstrip your mind is a recipe for a completely short burnout in the game. So first, forget approximately the concept of education every day, or instances a day education, or something else. Also, pass the idea of hour physical games that have you ever ever training until you puke. You're not organized for that, to be pretty sincere, and at this degree, it might be extra harm than tremendous for you besides.

For a starting powerlifter, the three keys to preserve in mind are moderation, improvement, and GPP. GPP stands for General Physical Preparation, and it's far pretty sincerely ensuring your body is in form sufficient to place it through the schooling which you want it to do. While superheavyweight powerlifters will often have a instead rotund appearance, the fact is that the out of shape fatty powerlifter is a difficulty of the past. Many powerlifters, particularly individuals who compete in weight lessons below 220 kilos, will activity at the least a stable center, if not defined abs and torsos.

Therefore, you may be following a 4 day per week lifting plan. These physical games are going to be sort of one hour or so (if you take longer than 75 mins, you are screwing spherical an excessive amount of inside the fitness center). Three of these exercising workout routines are going to be centered on constructing one of your opposition lifts, even as the fourth day is an afternoon of extensive lifting and GPP.

What about the other three days steady with week? Those are as plenty as you. Go play basketball. Go draw close out together with your children. Go to paintings. Whatever. Try to live active (no 24 hour Call of Duty marathons, ok?), however live sane. The excessive stages of willpower and way of life changes wanted for heavy duty powerlifting will come later down the street, even as and in case you are organized for them.

The first day of your exercising week is going to be the squat. Not wonderful is it the number one exercising completed in a meet, however it's also one of the maximum taxing at the frame. Let's get it out of the way first, while you are coming off of a relaxation day and also you aren't being overwhelmed down with the useful resource of manner of your week. Next may be the bench, then the deadlift, and in the end a popular body day. For your common lifter with a Monday to Friday interest, it have to appearance something like this:

Monday   Tuesday   Wednesday   Thursday Friday   Saturday   Sunday

Squat   Bench   Off   Deadlift   GPP   Off   Off

Of course for you, modifications to your artwork time desk and such are critical. Do not, but, try to cram 3 days of training proper in a row. Keep it to two on, one off, on, off, to permit your frame time to get better.

In addition to weekly cycles, a exquisite 12 week training plan might be broken down into 5 week mini cycles, and 2 weeks of deload/meet training at the quit. Some well-known programs and authors use 4 week month-to-month cycles alternatively, however for the purpose that calendar and a 4 week cycle in no manner line up except, you could discover that you can drift regardless. A five week cycle gives you greater time to make income and variations earlier than changing subjects up.

This is in which improvement is available in. You need to be striving to gain on every workout, even though it's miles exceptional by way of the usage of using one repetition or one pound over closing time. Keep statistics of your lifts, and ensure you tune them.

One problem that hasn't been addressed an excessive amount of in preceding chapters is GPP. The lifts used for GPP may be pretty a awesome deal something, and is based totally absolutely off of your very very own private options and weaknesses. The GPP day is also a notable day to do approach paintings, and to do highbrow schooling. The GPP workout must be at a far quicker pace than your most critical lifts exercising sporting events, to furthermore supply a similarly cardiovascular advantage.

Cardio education is some thing that isn't frequently related to powerlifters, for more than one reasons. First, the sort of extended, slow, slogging aerobic regularly finished through gymnasium goers is unfavourable to every restoration from heavy lifting, and might surely be catabolic in nature (it strips muscle some distance from the body). Since powerlifting is a hobby with repeated bouts of immoderate intensity, quick duration motion, your cardiovascular training need to additionally reflect that. Sprints, intervals, and other forms of exercise epitomize this sort of education.

Finally, for this template, in preference to going off of possibilities of a one rep max, go off of fee of perceived exertion. The RPE scale is going from a 1 at its lowest to 10 at its most. A actual 10 have to go away you with out the functionality to do one extra repetition. So if the template says 5 reps at a ten RPE, because of this that the fifth rep must be simply getting ready to seeing stars and passing out afterwards. This isn't always often completed, not handiest for protection's sake, but additionally for your frame's capability to get better.

General RPE Scale for Powerlifting

1-5 = You're now not operating. This intensity is used for warmups and method work nice

6-7 = A suitable degree for GPP lifting, and heavier technique art work. You experience the muscle running, but stop in advance than it receives definitely excessive.

eight = You need to crank out 2-three more reps inside the set in case you sincerely pushed yourself, however that might be the give up of the supply for that day.

9 = You enjoy you could optimistically do 1 extra, however 2 might be iffy.

10 = You've had been given not a few aspect left in the gasoline tank. You can't entire a few other rep with out failure.

A General 4 Day a Week Powerlifting Template

Day X: Focus

Exercise   Sets   Reps   Perceived Exertion Notes

Warm-up/Technique Work   3-8   3-5 This is used for every heat-u.S.And favored mobility paintings

Main Lift   X   eight

Main Lift   2   7   Same exercising, however strip away 20% of the load.

Accessory Lift 1   4   7

Accessory Lift 2   four   7

Now which you have a trendy template, permit's take a look at a way to gather the 12 week cycle. We referred to earlier that the 12 weeks may be broken down into two 5 week mini cycles, with a 2 week pre-meet recuperation period. The first 5 week mini cycle is built to feature amount and paintings functionality. As such, you may hold the weights the equal in your important lifts, however will try to upload repetitions each week.

The second mini-cycle is going the alternative direction. Instead of which includes repetitions, the focal point can be on inclusive of weight every set, while the use of shorter devices to build toward ordinary amount. Here's a fashionable breakdown by means of manner of week:

Week 1 2 three 4 five 6 7 eight 9 10 11 12

Sets/Reps three/five three/6 4/6 4/7 4/8
four/7 5/4 6/3 6/3 7/2 5/5 3/5

RPE eight 8 eight eight eight eight
nine 9 nine 9 6 6

Now, permit's positioned it together for you. While this template can be very usable as-is, you may want to regulate a number of the accent bodily sports to healthy the tool availability of your gymnasium or the ideal desires of your body.

Day 1/Week 1: Squats

Exercise Sets Reps Perceived Exertion Notes

Squats 3-8 15-3 three-5 Start with an empty bar, and upload weight slowly as much as 70% of work gadgets

Squats three five eight

Squats 2 10 7 Same exercising, but strip away 20% of the load.

Lunges 4 10 7

Hamstring Curls   4   12   7

Day 2/ Week 1: Bench Press

Exercise   Sets   Reps   Perceived Exertion Notes

Bench Press   three-eight   10-four   3-5   This is used for both warmups and elegant mobility artwork

Bench Press   3   five   8

Bench Press   2   10   7   Strip away 20% of the burden.

Dumbbell Incline Press   four   10   7

Pushups   4   15+   7

Day 3/ Week 1: Deadlift

Exercise   Sets   Reps   Perceived Exertion Notes

Deadlift   3-eight   3-4   three-5   This is used for every warmness-united statesand current mobility art work

Romanian Deadlift   3   five   eight

RDL 2 10 7 Strip away 20% of the weight.

Dumbbell Row 4 12 7

Pullups four Max 7

Day four/ Week 1: GPP

Exercise Sets Reps Perceived Exertion Notes

Bench Press three 10 five Technique Work

Box Squat three 10 5 Technique Work

Deadlift three 5 5 Technique Work

Dips/ Hanging Leg Raises/ Step Ups/ Bodyweight Rows three-four 10 7 The rest of the exercise want to be executed as a circuit, with 1 minute rest amongst circuits. You ought to do a entire of 3-four circuits

Day 1/Week 2: Squats

Exercise Sets Reps Perceived Exertion Notes

Squats   3-8   15-three   three-5   Start with an empty bar, and add weight slowly as an awful lot as 70% of exertions gadgets

Squats   three   6   eight

Squats   2   10   7   Same exercising, but strip away 20% of the load.

Front Squats   4   10   7

Hamstring Curls   four   12   7

Day 1/ Week 2: Bench Press

Exercise	Sets	Reps	Perceived Exertion	Notes
Bench Press	3-eight	10-4	three-5	This is used for each warmth-united statesand famous mobility paintings
Bench Press	three	5	eight	
Bench Press	2	10	7	Strip away 20% of the burden.
Decline Press	4	10	7	
Overhead Press	four	15+	7	

Day 3/ Week 2: Deadlift

Exercise	Sets	Reps	Perceived Exertion	Notes
Deadlift	three-eight	3-4	3-five	This is used for each warmness-u.S.A.And popular mobility paintings
Romanian Deadlift	three	five	eight	
RDL	2	10	7	Strip away 20% of the load.
Rack Pulls	4	12	7	
Lat Pulldown	four	Max	7	

Day 4/ Week 2: GPP

Exercise	Sets	Reps	Perceived Exertion	Notes
Bench Press	three	10	5	Technique Work
Box Squat	three	10	five	Technique Work
Deadlift	three	five	5	Technique Work
Pushups/ Burpees/ Bear Crawls/ Lunges	3-4	30 sec	7	The rest of the exercise ought to

be finished as a circuit, with 1 minute rest amongst circuits. You ought to do a entire of three-four circuits

Day 1/Week 3: Squats

Exercise   Sets   Reps   Perceived Exertion Notes

Squats   3-eight   15-three   three-five   Start with an empty bar, and add weight slowly as much as 70% of exertions sets

Squats   four   6   8

Squats   2   10   7   Same workout, but strip away 20% of the weight.

Bulgarian Split Squat   four   10   7

Hamstring Curls   4   12   7

Day 2/ Week three: Bench Press

Exercise   Sets   Reps   Perceived Exertion Notes

Bench Press   three-eight   10-4   3-five   This is used for each warmups and famous mobility artwork

Bench Press   3   five   8

Bench Press   2   10   7   Strip away 20% of the burden.

Banded Flat Bench   4   10   7

Lat Pulldowns   4   12   7

Day three/ Week 3: Deadlift

Exercise   Sets   Reps   Perceived Exertion Notes

Deadlift   3-eight   three-four   3-five   This is used for each warmups and standard mobility paintings

Romanian Deadlift   three   5   8

RDL   2   10   7   Strip away 20% of the load.

Barbell Row   four   12   7

Pullups   4   Max   7

Day 4/ Week 3: GPP

Exercise	Sets	Reps	Perceived Exertion	Notes
Bench Press	three	10	five	Technique Work
Box Squat	3	10	5	Technique Work
Deadlift	three	5	5	Technique Work
Dips/ Hanging Leg Raises/ Step Ups/ Bodyweight Rows	3-four	10	7	The relaxation of the exercise ought to be completed as a circuit, with 1 minute rest amongst circuits. You want to do a complete of 3-four circuits

Day 1/Week 4: Squats

Exercise	Sets	Reps	Perceived Exertion	Notes
Squats	3-eight	15-3	three-5	Start with an empty bar, and add weight slowly as a good deal as 70% of labor devices
Squats	four	7	eight	

Squats   2   10   7   Same exercise, but strip away 20% of the burden.

Hamstring Curls   4   10   7

Box Squats   4   12   7

Day 2/ Week 4: Bench Press

Exercise   Sets   Reps   Perceived Exertion Notes

Bench Press   3-eight   10-4   3-five   This is used for each warmups and exceptional mobility artwork

Bench Press   4   7   eight

Bench Press   2   10   7   Strip away 20% of the load.

Incline Press   4   10   7

Dips   4   15+   7

Day three/ Week 4: Deadlift

Exercise   Sets   Reps   Perceived Exertion Notes

Deadlift   three-eight   three-four   3-five   This is used for each warmups and preferred mobility paintings

Romanian Deadlift   four   7   eight

RDL   2   10   7   Strip away 20% of the load.

Banded Rows   four   12   7

Lat Pulldowns   four   Max   7

Day four/ Week 4: GPP

Exercise	Sets	Reps	Perceived Exertion	Notes
Bench Press	three	10	five	Technique Work
Box Squat	3	10	five	Technique Work
Deadlift	3	5	five	Technique Work

Sledgehammer Tires/ Dragging Sled/ Farmer's Walk/ Burpees   four-5   forty five sec   7   The rest of the exercise need to be finished as a circuit, with 1 minute rest among circuits. You need to do a complete of four-5 circuits

Day 1/Week 5: Squats

Note: Week five is a transition/recovery week, so great the precept lifts themselves and GPP is professional

Exercise   Sets   Reps   Perceived Exertion   Notes

Squats   three-eight   15-three   three-5   Start with an empty bar, and upload weight slowly up to 70% of labor devices

Squats   four   8   8

Squats   2   10   7   Same exercise, however strip away 20% of the weight.

Day 2/ Week five: Bench Press

Exercise   Sets   Reps   Perceived Exertion   Notes

Bench Press   3-8   10-4   3-5   This is used for every warmups and fashionable mobility paintings

Bench Press   4   eight   8

Bench Press   2   10   7   Strip away 20% of the load.

Day three/ Week five: Deadlift

Exercise	Sets	Reps	Perceived Exertion	Notes
Deadlift	3-8	three-4	3-five	This is used for every warmups and fashionable mobility work
Romanian Deadlift	4	8	eight	
RDL	2	10	7	Strip away 20% of the burden.

Day four/ Week five: GPP

Exercise	Sets	Reps	Perceived Exertion	Notes
Bench Press	three	10	5	Technique Work
Box Squat	three	10	5	Technique Work
Deadlift	3	5	five	Technique Work
Pushups/ Hanging Leg Raises/ Step Ups/ Bodyweight Rows	3-4	20 sec	7	The rest of the workout want to be accomplished as a

circuit, with 1 minute rest amongst circuits. You need to do a whole of 3-4 circuits

Day 1/Week 6: Squats

Exercise   Sets   Reps   Perceived Exertion Notes

Squats   3-8   15-3   3-5   Start with an empty bar, and upload weight slowly as a good deal as 70% of exertions gadgets

Squats   four   7   eight   The first set have to be at the equal weight as Week 5. Add five-10 kilos regular with set.

Squats   2   10   7   Same workout, however strip away 20% of the load.

Front Squats   four   10   7

Hamstring Curls   4   12   7

Day 2/ Week 6: Bench Press

Exercise   Sets   Reps   Perceived Exertion Notes

Bench Press   3-8   10-four   three-5   This is used for each warmups and elegant mobility art work

Bench Press   4   7   8   The first set need to be at the same weight as Week five. Add 2.Five-5 pounds constant with set.

Bench Press   2   10   7   Strip away 20% of the load.

Dumbbell Incline Press   4   10   7

Pushups   four   15+   7

Day 3/ Week 6: Deadlift

Exercise   Sets   Reps   Perceived Exertion Notes

Deadlift   three-8   3-four   three-5   This is used for both warmups and general mobility art work

Romanian Deadlift   4   7   8   The first set need to be at the identical weight as Week 5. Add 5-10 pounds in step with set.

RDL   2   10   7   Strip away 20% of the load.

Dumbbell Row   4   10   7

Reverse Flyes   4   12   7

Day four/ Week 6: GPP

Exercise	Sets	Reps	Perceived Exertion	Notes
Bench Press	3	10	five	Technique Work
Box Squat	3	10	5	Technique Work
Deadlift	three	five	5	Technique Work
Pushups/ Bodyweight Squat Jumps/ 1 Leg Glute Bridges/ Mountain Climbers	three-4	20	7	

The rest of the workout should be accomplished as a circuit, with 1 minute relaxation among circuits. You need to do a whole of 3-four circuits

Day 1/Week 7: Squats

Exercise   Sets   Reps   Perceived Exertion Notes

Squats three-eight 15-three 3-5 Start with an empty bar, and upload weight slowly as much as 70% of hard work units

Squats 5 four 9 The first set need to be on the same weight as final set Week 6. Add five-10 pounds in step with set.

Squats 2 10 7 Same exercise, however strip away 30% of the weight.

Bulgarian Split Squats four 10 7

GHR/Reverse Hyper 4 12 7

Day 2/ Week 7: Bench Press

Exercise   Sets   Reps   Perceived Exertion Notes

Bench Press three-eight 10-four 3-5 This is used for each warmups and ultra-modern mobility artwork

Bench Press four 5 9 The first set should be on the identical weight because the final set of Week 6. Add 2.Five-5 pounds in line with set.

Bench Press   2   10   7   Strip away 30% of the weight.

Dips   four   10   7

Pushups   4   15+   7

Day 3/ Week 7: Deadlift

Exercise   Sets   Reps   Perceived Exertion Notes

Deadlift   three-eight   3-four   3-5   This is used for both warmups and modern day mobility paintings

Romanian Deadlift   four   five   9   The first set need to be at the same weight due to the fact the pinnacle weight of Week 6. Add 5-10 kilos consistent with set.

RDL   2   10   7   Strip away 20% of the burden.

Dumbbell Row   four   10   7

Reverse Flyes   four   12   7

Day 4/ Week 7: GPP

Exercise	Sets	Reps	Perceived Exertion	Notes
Bench Press	three	10	5	Technique Work
Box Squat	3	10	five	Technique Work
Deadlift	three	5	five	Technique Work
Burpees				
Bear Crawls	5-7	45 seconds	7	The relaxation of the exercising want to be finished as a circuit, with 1 minute relaxation among circuits. You ought to do a whole of three-four circuits

Day 1/Week eight: Squats

Exercise	Sets	Reps	Perceived Exertion	Notes
Squats	three-8	15-three	3-5	Start with an empty bar, and add weight slowly as an awful lot as 70% of tough paintings gadgets
Squats	6	3	nine	See Week 7 Notes

Squats   2   10   7   Same workout, however strip away 20% of the burden.

Box Squats   4   10   7

Hamstring Curls   four   12   7

Day 2/ Week eight: Bench Press

Exercise   Sets   Reps   Perceived Exertion Notes

Bench Press   3-8   10-four   3-5   This is used for both warmups and fashionable mobility artwork

Bench Press   6   3   nine   See Week 7 Notes

Bench Press   2   10   7   Strip away 20% of the load.

Decline Bench   4   10   7

Incline Bench   four   15+   7

Day three/ Week 8: Deadlift

Exercise   Sets   Reps   Perceived Exertion Notes

Deadlift three-eight 3-4 three-5 This is used for each warmups and fashionable mobility paintings

Romanian Deadlift 6 three nine See Week 7 Notes

RDL 2 10 7 Strip away 20% of the burden.

Lat Pulldown 4 10 7

GHR four 12 7

Day four/ Week 8: GPP

Exercise Sets Reps Perceived Exertion Notes

Bench Press 3 10 five Technique Work

Box Squat 3 10 5 Technique Work

Deadlift three five 5 Technique Work

Pushups/ Bodyweight Squat Jumps/ 1 Leg Glute Bridges/ Mountain Climbers 3-4 20 7 The relaxation of the exercising should be accomplished as a circuit, with 1 minute relaxation among circuits. You need to do a whole of 3-four circuits

Day 1/Week nine: Squats

Exercise   Sets   Reps   Perceived Exertion   Notes

Squats 3-eight 15-three three-5 Start with an empty bar, and add weight slowly as plenty as 70% of difficult work units

Squats 6 three nine See Week 7 Notes

Squats 2 10 7 Same workout, however strip away 20% of the burden.

Front Squats four 10 7

Hamstring Curls 4 12 7

Day 2/ Week 9: Bench Press

Exercise   Sets   Reps   Perceived Exertion   Notes

Bench Press three-eight 10-4 three-five This is used for every warmups and modern day mobility artwork

Bench Press   6   three   9   See Week 7 Notes

Bench Press   2   10   7   Strip away 20% of the load.

Dumbbell Incline Press   four   10   7

Pushups   four   15+   7

Day three/ Week 9: Deadlift

Exercise   Sets   Reps   Perceived Exertion Notes

Deadlift   3-eight   3-4   three-5   This is used for each warmups and stylish mobility paintings

Romanian Deadlift   6   three   9   See Week 7 Notes

RDL   2   10   7   Strip away 20% of the load.

GHR   four   10   7

Barbell Low Row   four   12   7

Day four/ Week 9: GPP

Exercise Sets Reps Perceived Exertion Notes

Bench Press three 10 5 Technique Work

Box Squat 3 10 five Technique Work

Deadlift three five five Technique Work

one hundred meter Sprint/ 60 sec. Leg Raises/ one hundred meter Bear Crawl/ 30 Sec. Pushups 3-4 NA 7 The relaxation of the workout should be completed as a circuit, with 1 minute rest amongst circuits. You ought to do an entire of 3-4 circuits

Day 1/Week 10: Squats

Exercise Sets Reps Perceived Exertion Notes

Squats three-eight 15-three 3-5 Start with an empty bar, and upload weight slowly up to 70% of labor gadgets

Squats 7 2 9 See Week 7 Notes

Squats 2 10 7 Same exercise, however strip away 40% of the weight.

Front Squats   four   10   7

Hamstring Curls   4   12   7

Day 2/ Week 10: Bench Press

Exercise   Sets   Reps   Perceived Exertion
Notes

Bench Press   three-8   10-4   3-5   This is used
for each warmups and brand new mobility
paintings

Bench Press   7   2   nine   See Week 7 Notes

Bench Press   2   10   7   Strip away 40% of the
weight.

Incline Press   four   10   7

Dumbbell Flat Bench   four   15   7

Day three/ Week 10: Deadlift

Exercise   Sets   Reps   Perceived Exertion
Notes

Deadlift   three-8   3-four   three-5   This is
used for every warmups and fashionable
mobility art work

173

Romanian Deadlift   7   2   nine   See Week 7 Notes

RDL   2   10   7   Strip away forty% of the load.

Bodyweight Row   4   10+   7

1 Arm Dumbbell Row   four   12   7

Day 4/ Week 10: GPP

Exercise   Sets   Reps   Perceived Exertion Notes

Bench Press   three   10   five   Technique Work

Box Squat   3   10   five   Technique Work

Deadlift   three   5   five   Technique Work

Pushups/ Bodyweight Squat Jumps/ 1 Leg Glute Bridges/ Mountain Climbers   three-4   20   7   The rest of the exercise ought to be accomplished as a circuit, with 1 minute relaxation among circuits. You ought to do a whole of 3-4 circuits

Day 1/Week 11: Squats

Week eleven is the number one of backoff weeks. Intensity is taken down, to permit the body to recover from such hard work the past 10 weeks

Exercise   Sets   Reps   Perceived Exertion Notes

Squats three-eight 15-three 3-5 Start with an empty bar, and add weight slowly as an awful lot as 70% of labor devices

Squats 5 5 6

Front Squats four 10 7

Hamstring Curls 4 12 7

Day 2/ Week 11: Bench Press

Exercise   Sets   Reps   Perceived Exertion Notes

Bench Press three-8 10-4 3-5 This is used for each warmups and famous mobility paintings

Bench Press five five 6

Dumbbell Incline Press   four   10   7

Pushups   4   15+   7

Day 3/ Week 11: Deadlift

Exercise   Sets   Reps   Perceived Exertion
Notes

Deadlift   3-eight   3-four   three-5   This is
used for each warmups and stylish mobility
art work

Deadlift   five   5   6

Dumbbell Row   four   10   7

Reverse Flyes   four   12   7

Chapter 16: Frequent Program Questions

Q: Can I alternative (some thing) in vicinity of the usage of what is inside the template?

A: Yes and no. For approach work, you MUST do the competition lifts. This is not negotiable. If you're unwilling or not capable of do the method art work, then powerlifting competition isn't for you. You can use the template to get more potent, but you sincerely aren't ready or perhaps able to do competition.

That being said, you may alternative accent lifts at your discretion. Just ensure that the lifts are 1) multi-joint (this isn't always a bodybuilding software program), 2) running the desired muscle organizations for the skilled carry of the day, and 3) is trackable.

Q: There are not any tool lifts on the software program. Why?

A: Machines have their vicinity in education applications. That being stated, powerlifting is competed the use of barbells and plates. Get used to the feeling of getting actual barbells on your palms or throughout your shoulders. In addition, not all machines are created equal. A appropriate tool may be of superb benefit as an accessory raise, at the same time as a horrible one is beneficial for little more than a towel rack.

Q: Where is the aerobic paintings? I want to drop weight to get into the splendor I need.

A: Let's get one factor immediately right away. Cardio paintings does no longer drop weight. Diet drops weight. What you install your mouth overrides nearly any level of labor finished with either the weights or in aerobic (Olympic athletes like Michael Phelps but). Doing cardio on each your rest days or after lifting can be finished for famous health (in fact it could help with recuperation), however it's far no substitute for an extremely good healthy healthy eating plan.

Q: What approximately slicing weight via sweating, or saunas?

A: This approach is used by many better diploma powerlifters to get those final three-four kilos off. However, till you've got were given in advance enjoy with this method from sports activities activities together with wrestling or specific weight class sports activities, pass it till you apprehend how your body feels at some point of a powerlifting meet. Meets are already hard bodily demanding situations, there is no want to compound the issue proper off the bat.

Q: Is this template repeatable?

A: Yes. If you aren't going to do a powerlifting meet at the prevent of week 12, then update the week 12 method week with a check week. Find your personal bests inside the squat, the bench, and deadlift, and use the ones new benchmarks as starting factors over the subsequent 12 week cycle.

Q: I'm sore in my (muscle institution). What is the excellent way to get rid of this ache?

A: The first way to alleviate muscular pain is to do mobility artwork, and gentle tissue rub down. Active restoration, rub down chairs, and precise strategies are the wonderful idea. While the usage of ache relievers such as aspirin or ibuprofen may additionally help within the quick time period, it's far satisfactory to find out the motive of the ache and proper away paintings on that. If the pain is because of terrible approach, spend the greater time stretching and operating on getting your method best.

Chapter 17: The Powerlifting Meet

You've busted your butt for the past 3 months. You assume you've got your method down, and you are excited to do your first powerlifting meet. Now what?

The first element to realize it that powerlifting meets are a actual take a look at of muscular patience. In eventually, over the route of what's going to be as short as 3 or four hours or as long as nine or 10 hours, you'll warmth up and attempt as plenty as nine maximal try lifts. This takes huge quantities of bodily and intellectual fortitude.

The first step for purchasing meet organized must be finished as fast as you apprehend what meet you want to compete in. Find out the fundamentals from the meet coordinator, collectively with wherein the meet is going on, the front expenses, and instances for weigh-ins, heat-ups, and other incidentals. If the meet is neighborhood or inside using distance, coordinate with a chum or member of the family on driving (the use of on the equal time as dieting, or after a meet, isn't always a strong concept). If you need to get a lodge room, make reservations. In addition, if some issue that can be paid earlier, do it. When meet day comes, your whole recognition wants to be on lifting.

When it includes weigh-ins, try to do it as early as possible. Many massive meets even have weigh-ins the night time time time earlier than, which allows you to consume and fuel up earlier. Quite a few horror memories had been suggested thru buffet consuming locations after being invaded via using corporations of weight loss plan powerlifters who simply completed weigh-ins. If the weigh-ins are the day of the meet, try to supply your self as lots time as you could to refuel, to rehydrate, and to loosen up earlier than you need to heat up.

Two days previous to the meet (in reality, as brief as your final exercise is finished), you need to p.C. Your tools in its very own bag. In the bag, you ought to have at a minimal your belt, your lifting shoes, and your competition clothes. Other common devices encompass sports activities sports drinks, snacks, a spare set of clothing (competition apparel in case you feasible), a sweat in shape for the time in between lifts, and MP3 gamers. Check this bag earlier than you go away for the meet. While powerlifters are in current day a nice organization of human beings, few are inclined to lend out their belts or shoes to a stranger for the duration of a meet, even in case you favored to attempt to raise in unexpected equipment.

On meet day, after checking in, there will maximum probable be a tips assembly. These can be rather easy, however pay interest. The judges will circulate over their instructions, how flights might be set up, and exclusive data that you may discover critical.

After the regulations assembly, you may have a threat to warm temperature up and test in with the scoring table. At the desk you could offer your starting strive weights for every increase, similarly to file your settings for the squat stands and bench press. When choosing an opening weight for every convey, choose out out a weight that is about ninety% of your maximum for the squat and bench, and about 80 five% for the deadlift. A exact target is to apply the weights you used inside the direction of week 10 of your training cycle. Remember, you can regularly regulate your weights later based totally off of strategies your warm temperature-usago.

It's then time to each loosen up out, or heat up, depending on your function within the meet. Early flights have a propensity to be lighter weights, so that you will maximum probably be squatting early. Take the time to stretch, warm temperature up, after which artwork as tons as about 80-eighty five% of your beginning weight. Depending on how that weight feels, you could adjust your first attempt. If you are not in the first flight of lifters, do a gentle desired warmup, and begin warming up your squats about 10-15 minutes earlier than you observed you'll be organized. A accurate rule of thumb is at the same time as the flight previous to yours is prepared halfway via with their second strive is a great time to start warming up your very very personal squats.